D1104640

Units, Dimensions, and Dimensionless Numbers

UNITS, DIMENSIONS, AND DIMENSIONLESS NUMBERS

D. C. IPSEN

Associate Research Engineer
University of California

McGRAW-HILL BOOK COMPANY, INC.

New York   Toronto   London   1960

UNITS, DIMENSIONS, AND DIMENSIONLESS NUMBERS

32030

Preface

The aim of this book is to show how a full understanding of units and dimensions provides a simple basis for explaining aspects of physical description that otherwise may seem confusing or mysterious. The way units and dimensions behave—in particular, the way their properties influence the mathematical description of physical behavior—makes sense only if certain basic notions and conventions are recognized. Once these are recognized, the strange quirks and uncanny powers of units and dimensions at once become easy to comprehend and simple to control.

An understanding of units and dimensions is easily acquired if one takes the trouble; however, it is often not obvious that trouble needs to be taken. An engineer or scientist inevitably gains familiarity with units, and perhaps with dimensions as well, through continual contact. Such familiarity, however, may often be an obstacle to understanding: if one becomes too familiar with an idea, one may easily overlook the fact that there is anything to be understood. To understand the workings of units and dimensions, one must avoid the error of assuming that the sense behind familiar notions is obvious.

Like any book on units and dimensions, this book spends some time on questions of technique. Techniques of handling units, techniques of discovering the requirements for similitude, and techniques of dimensional analysis are presented. An effort is made, however, to present the techniques as no more than a systematic way to follow the dictates of logic: that is, to emphasize that technique is an outcome of understanding rather than a basis for it.

It is not the intention of this book to record the many conflicting viewpoints that are held on the subject of units and dimensions. Although certain dissident notions are considered—in fact, I may occasionally be guilty of flogging dead horses—no attempt is made to give a complete description of the many modes of thought that have been proposed. The aim of the book is to present what appears to be the proper viewpoint when judged in terms of what we normally do; its conclusions may therefore occasionally disagree with what others have argued we should do.

Most chapters of the book are followed by problems. Certain of these—particularly if they supplement the ideas of the text or provide especially effective examples of the application of these ideas—are worked out in detail. The last two chapters, although they have unifying motives and present concepts that are probably not easily deduced from the preceding chapters, are to a large extent an excuse for presenting further examples of the use of ideas presented before. Problems and examples therefore do not follow these chapters.

The book has been helped along the path from initial idea to publication by several besides the writer. I am particularly grateful to Prof. L. M. Grossman of the University of California at Berkeley for his stimulating criticism of the final draft. I am also indebted to Prof.

R. M. Drake, Jr., of Princeton University for his encouraging review of an earlier version. The greatest help, however, has come from my wife. Her most conspicuous contribution, though not the largest, has been the typing of the many drafts that were necessary in the evolution of the book.

D. C. Ipsen

Contents

Units, Dimensions, and Dimensionless Numbers

1

The Description of Physical Ideas

1-1 Introduction

For most of us the notion that physical ideas may be described mathematically is a notion that we can't remember ever being without. At our first contact, mathematics is made "meaningful" by representing it as a description of the physical world. Addition or subtraction is likely to have citrus overtones; division is conceived with the help of a pastry chef. While most of us progress beyond the point where we must visualize oranges before we can succeed in adding 2 to 3 or mentally cut a pie into four pieces before we can divide by 4, few of us reach the point where we feel that we can understand mathematics that isn't quite closely bound to some physical conception.

Our early contacts with the mathematical description of the physical world always involve some sort of counting procedure. We proceed from counting oranges to counting pennies and dollars to counting how many years Mary is older than Jane to counting units of

1

length or time. Although the abstractions of mathematics may puzzle us, we meet no conceptual difficulty in translating a physical idea into numbers. As we encounter more sophisticated physical descriptions, however, we are likely to forget that all we really have learned is how to count. We assign numbers to physical ideas without always being fully aware of what it is we are counting: in fact, we may even lose our juvenile notion that counting is involved. We tend to lose sight, in other words, of the mathematical meaning of our physical descriptions.

Even though we may succeed in clinging to the notion that any number that we attach to a physical idea serves to count some sort of unit, we are likely to become increasingly confused about the meaning of a unit. This confusion is increased as we recognize that the units themselves may come in for mathematical treatment. We may find it easy, for example, to conceive of acceleration as being described by the increase in the number of feet traveled in successive seconds and to recognize a counting procedure in this description; however, our concept of counting units to define acceleration hardly prepares us for combining the units counted into the mathematical arrangement ft/sec^2 when we come to designate the unit of acceleration. Some new notion has clearly intruded since our days of counting oranges; and unless we recognize what this notion is, the stage is set for confusion.

Confusion manifests itself in two somewhat distinct ways. We first are liable to be perplexed by the way that units behave. If we impute to them a mathematical meaning, we find that they behave in a rational manner much of the time, but occasionally we find that they behave in a manner that seems to dispute conventional logic. We find, in other words, that "common sense" explains their behavior up to a point, but beyond that point some uncommon notions seem to be called for. We are able to side-step the issue by the expedient of learning more or less by rote how to handle each special situation; but the confusion remains even though the consternation may be dispelled.

Perhaps more confusing is the remarkable influence that we find units to possess in guiding the formulation of physical relations. By looking at the units (or conventionally the dimensions) of physical variables, we are able to make important deductions about how the variables must enter a physical relationship. In a seemingly mysterious manner, the way in which units are related influences the way in which the physical variables that they describe are related. While we are likely to be merely confused by the way that units behave, we are likely to be quite mystified by the way that they exert influence on physical formulations. Even though we may gain considerable familiarity with both the behavior and the influence of units, few of us can lose completely an apprehension about them.

The chief aim of this book is to look closely and carefully at the meaning implicit in the units and dimensions that we assign to physical variables. The confusion about the behavior of units and the mystery about their influence on the formulation of physical relations are easily dispelled: the only requirement is that we recognize the full implications of conventional description. These implications are not always conspicuous, and they are likely to have unexpected and obscure manifestations; but once they are recognized the confusion and mystery evaporate.

Definite rules guide our description of physical concepts and physical behavior. Although we cannot go far in a study of physical science without seeing these rules in operation, we may easily go quite a distance without recognizing the generality of the rules or perceiving their full meaning. Too often we approach each new physical description as a unique statement, forgetting that it is usually made in the context of established conventions. Unless the nature of these conventions and the pervasion of their influence are recognized, we are understandably perplexed.

Before worrying about the many details and nuances of physical description, it may be helpful to look briefly at the broad outlines. We are basically concerned with two interrelated problems: how a physical concept is properly described, and how physical behavior is properly described.

1-2   The Nature of Physical Variables

A physical variable, in the restricted sense that we shall use, is any physical concept to which a numerical magnitude may be assigned. Many observable aspects of nature will not, by this definition, fall into the category of physical variables. As an example, for a potable liquid we may assign appropriate numbers to describe its density, its temperature, its viscosity, etc.—and we would consider such variables in the class of physical variables; however, we are at present unable to use such a mode of description for its taste or its bouquet, and we would therefore not class these properties—in the present context—as physical variables. In other words, as we shall interpret it, the term physical variable properly denotes a physical concept that is described mathematically.

The physical variables that we use are of two significantly different sorts. The sort of variable that probably first comes to mind—variables such as mass, length, time, velocity, area, viscosity, and so on—we shall class as substantial variables. Characteristic of such variables is the need for some artificial physical standard in terms of which they may be expressed. Normally we describe a substantial physical variable by reference to a standard unit. The unit represents—or should represent—a precise magnitude of the physical variable described, suitable as a basis for describing other magnitudes.

An important class of physical variables, however, require no such artificial standards. These are what we shall call natural variables. They derive their meaning from the physical system they describe without reference to any external standard. Natural variables are also called dimensionless variables or dimensionless numbers. Why this name is deserved will be evident later.

The simplest natural variables are mere ratios of substantial variables of the same sort. As an example, the slenderness or fineness of a missile—which is defined as the ratio of its length to its diameter—can clearly be defined without reference to a bar of platinum growing hoary in some bureau of standards. The ratio effectively describes the length in terms of the diameter as a unit, and therefore no artificial unit need be involved. Similarly the Mach number at which the missile travels—the ratio of its speed to the speed of sound in the medium through which it travels—is a natural variable needing no external standard.

Not all natural variables are as obviously natural as these. Many natural variables involve combinations of substantial variables that are not of the same sort. It is not superficially obvious, for example, that the speed of the missile times its length times the ratio of the density to viscosity for the medium through which it travels is a natural variable. But this variable, the Reynolds number, can be shown—in the proper context—to be just as natural as the Mach number.

The proper definition of a physical variable, as well as the distinction between the substantial and the natural variable, is most easily arrived at by a study of units. The first part of the book is mainly concerned with this study. After a general discussion of the nature of units and the associated concept of dimensions, the principal units and dimensions of mechanics, thermodynamics and heat transfer, and electricity are looked at in some detail. The study is chiefly directed at discovering how units are interrelated and is not directly concerned with how the physical standard that defines a unit is set up and maintained: although theoretical considerations that guide the creation of a standard are within our present concern, the practical considerations for the most part are not. Our primary interest is in the mathematical nature of units and the variables they serve to define—and eventually in how the recognition of this nature influences the formulation of physical relationships.

1-3 The Nature of Physical Relationships

An accurate understanding of the meaning of a physical variable and a clear distinction between the substantial variable and the natural variable—in other words, the presumed goals of our study of units and dimensions—are of practical value only because of the involvement of these concepts in the equations or relations that describe physical behavior. The reason for defining the physical variable is for the sake of defining what description of nature may be treated mathematically; and the reason for distinguishing between substantial and natural variables is that they fill somewhat different roles in the description of physical facts.

To describe a physical state or circumstance, we normally rely on substantial physical variables. These are the variables that we use for the measurement of tangible concepts. By combining the substantial variables appropriately, we may usually define a smaller number of natural variables; however, the natural variables so defined are essentially superfluous to the mere physical description. Ordinarily—though not inevitably—it is the substantial variables that are of direct practical interest.

But when we set out to find how the substantial variables are related, we are likely to find that the natural variable assumes a role of great importance. Most physical relations have the property of being expressible in terms of natural variables alone. Therefore, though we may need a large number of substantial variables to provide a full description of a physical circumstance, we need only a smaller number of natural variables to provide a full description of a physical relation. The natural variable, therefore, though of little value in describing a physical circumstance, is of great value in predicting it.

The usefulness of the natural variable in describing physical relations has led to the introduction into the vocabulary of engineering and science of a large number of variables that would probably not otherwise be in existence. Besides the many personalized numbers such as Reynolds number and Mach number, there are numbered among the natural variables a host of factors such as friction factor or power factor, of coefficients such as flow coefficient or restitution coefficient, and of efficiencies such as thermal efficiency or hydraulic efficiency. In the final analysis all these natural variables owe their existence to their role in describing physical relationships. It may be argued that some of them can claim an independent right to life as some sort of measure of merit; however, to define merit is to establish—or endeavor to establish—a physical relationship.

The latter part of the book is mainly concerned with the nature of physical relationships, and therefore with the natural variable. The basis for describing physical relationships in terms of natural variables is revealed, and then the problem of discovering what natural variables are involved in specific situations is attacked from several angles. Following this is an interpretation of the meaning and a demonstration of the use of a number of the natural variables encountered in fluid mechanics and heat transfer. The field considered in these applications is restricted in scope but is rich in examples of the use of natural variables; the difficulty in the mathematical analysis of fluid mechanics and heat transfer has proved a spur to the full exploitation of the basic notions of physical description. One may anticipate, therefore, that a study of just the natural variables of this field will provide quite a complete picture of how natural variables may be constructed, interpreted, and handled.

The ultimate aim of the book is to demonstrate how an adherence to certain rules simplifies the handling and formulation of physical description. By recognizing the common ingredients in physical description we may make generalizations that not only assist the practical business of dealing with physical variables and the relations they enter but also provide a basis for important theoretical conclusions. The goal of our study— like the ultimate goal of any scientific endeavor—is to uncover and illuminate these generalizations.

2
The Physical Nature of Units

2-1 Introduction

Unless we stop to ponder the notion, we are inclined to think of a unit as merely any identifying label that we attach to a physical magnitude to indicate the basis for its measurement. But as the name suggests, the unit deserves a more restricted meaning; and a more precise interpretation is clearly essential if we are to make any statements of general validity about units.

In this chapter we consider the physical meaning of units, and in the next we consider the mathematical meaning. Inevitably our physical interpretation is influenced by our eventual mathematical aims; and our mathematical treatment is similarly responsive to our physical notions. As a consequence neither the physical story nor the mathematical story can comfortably stand on its own. Some of the notions of the present chapter, therefore, may seem a bit arbitrary or unnecessary until the demands of mathematics are recognized.

2-2 The Meaning of Units

Properly defined, a unit is a selected magnitude of a physical variable in terms of which other magnitudes of the same variable may be described. Although some physical variables may not seem susceptible to this sort of description, it may reasonably be argued that any properly defined physical variable can be described in this manner. In other words, the number describing any proper physical variable simply indicates how many times the unit used in the description must be reduplicated (or subdivided) to match the magnitude of the physical variable.

Such an interpretation of the meaning of physical magnitudes is easy enough to accept for variables such as mass, length, or time. With variables of this sort—which are classed as extensive variables—larger amounts may clearly be formed by adding up smaller amounts, and the idea of a unit is completely natural. There is no strain in conceiving of a length of 5 feet as being simply a fivefold reduplication of a length unit of 1 foot.

The interpretation of variables such as density, viscosity, or temperature in terms of units is less obvious. Such variables—classed as intensive variables—do not add up in an obvious way. As an example, if one defined a unit density by reference to water at specified conditions, one could not then say a density of five units is simply a fivefold reduplication of the unit so defined. Clearly, any amount of the defining water added together will still have a density of one unit.

Most intensive variables, however, are defined in a manner that makes them proportional to extensive variables. As a consequence it becomes a simple matter to conceive of such variables—even though intensive in themselves—as describable in terms of a reduplicated unit. Density, for example, may be defined as mass per unit volume; and since mass is easily conceived in terms of units, density may be also. If a unit density represents a unit mass per unit volume, then five units of density represent five units of mass per unit volume. So for density, as for other intensive concepts, the unit being reduplicated is really an extensive unit.

For some intensive variables the relationship to an extensive concept is less obvious, or perhaps completely concealed. As the unit of absolute temperature is normally defined, for example, its proportionality to an extensive unit is not conspicuous. The definition of temperature establishes a technique for finding the ratio of two temperatures; from this knowledge, a temperature scale may then be constructed by assigning an arbitrary value to the temperature at some chosen physical condition or by assigning an arbitrary value to the temperature difference between two such conditions. The idea that a scale of this nature can be regarded as the representation of a reduplicated unit seems at first glance to be inappropriate. But even here it turns out that support can be found for this notion. Under suitable restrictions, absolute temperature may be regarded as equal to the heat transfer per unit of entropy increase. Since heat is an extensive concept, it may then be argued that the increment of the temperature scale deserves the name of unit. A doubled temperature would mean that twice as many units of heat transfer would be required to effect the same entropy change. The argument might seem to be somewhat blunted by the fact that entropy normally draws its definition from temperature rather than the other way around—but it doesn't have to be that way.

Although it is characteristic of the unit of an intensive variable that it has a tie with an extensive concept, that concept is occasionally defined only implicitly. Such a circumstance is often encountered when a physical variable is defined by a scale of values. Scale increments may often be established by some arbitrary scheme and may bear no direct relation to any previously conceived extensive concept. Although one cannot help feeling that any useful intensive concept probably earns its full usefulness because its unit may be related to a significant extensive property of the system described, the formal definition of a unit does not require such a tie: any proper scale of values may be conceived of as defining a unit. Of course the mere erection of a scale of values against which a physical variable may be compared may not give a proper scale. The scale must be capable of arbitrary subdivision to provide a full description of a physical variable. Since subdivision is a unique property of an extensive variable, the possibility of subdivision points to the existence—even though perhaps tacit—of an associated extensive concept. We may conclude, therefore, that, if the requirement of divisibility is met, there is no reason why scale increments cannot be regarded as defining a unit, even though an independent definition of the unit is not available. The evident truth is that a scale must define a unit if it is to provide more than a qualitative description. Only if interpreted in terms of units do relative values on a scale take on a quantitative significance: the presumption of a unit is essential to the complete definition of the variable described.

For good reasons—even though some may seem at this point a bit vague or at least difficult to enunciate— we therefore conclude that the unit is essential to the proper description of a physical variable and that any proper physical magnitude may be interpreted as describing the number of times a unit is reduplicated.

2-3   The Units of Discrete Variables

Physical variables that describe discrete events or entities would appear to constitute a somewhat special class of variables not conforming to all the foregoing remarks. As an example, to describe the number of trees in a forest one would normally use a single tree as a unit. Although the unit may be reduplicated without question, it can't be subdivided in an obvious manner, as we expect of any proper unit. Whether arbitrary subdivision of a discrete variable makes good sense or not, however, we normally don't restrain ourselves if the occasion demands. Despite obvious conceptual difficulties, when discrete variables are treated mathematically, they are normally treated as if continuous. In so far as such a treatment is appropriate, we may then reasonably apply the concepts that we associate with continuous variables directly to discrete variables. We recognize that such a viewpoint is artificial and are not troubled—at any rate, nine and a half out of ten of us are not troubled—by the physically meaningless concept of a fraction of an indivisible entity.

2-4   The Sign of Physical Variables

The idea that any physical variable is properly represented by a reduplicated unit might seem to lose some of its firmness when confronted by a negative variable. Clearly a unit cannot be reduplicated a negative number of times. One might imagine—and in fact a plausible argument may be made to support this notion—that a negative number may never properly describe any valid physical variable.

Such a rigid interpretation, however, is unnecessary, and would occasionally prove extremely awkward. It is frequently convenient and occasionally necessary to refer a concept to an arbitrary datum: in other words, to specify that the concept has zero magnitude as some condition other than its natural (or absolute) zero. Smaller physical amounts than the amount labeled zero then quite naturally are regarded as negative. All that is meant by the negative sign is that the unit involved must be subtracted the requisite number of times from the datum condition to get the condition described.

This possibility of picking a datum arbitrarily introduces another source of confusion into the meaning of a physical variable. If a particular concept is given a different datum, it effectively becomes a new concept. As an example, if we describe a mountain peak as having an elevation of 14,000 ft above sea level, but only 2,000 ft above the surrounding terrain, we have clearly described two different ideas; though the general concept of elevation is involved in each description, the altered datum gives a different meaning to the specific descriptions. Two variables that describe the same state—in the example, the vertical location of the peak—effectively describe different concepts if they employ different datums in the description. As a less obvious example, although temperatures of 15°C and 59°F denote the same condition, they are properly regarded as different physical variables. For two different units to describe the same concept, there is the clear necessity that the measurement of the concept in terms of either unit must start at the same point.

2-5 Concept Labels

The label attached to the magnitude of a physical variable is not always merely a unit. It may serve partly or wholly to define the physical concept: that is, it may serve to identify the concept being described rather than the unit in which it is measured. The distinction between a true unit and a concept label can easily be recognized from an example. In expressing a pressure measured in pounds per square inch one commonly attaches a label lb per sq in. absolute or alternatively lb per sq in. gage to the magnitude. The last word of the label indicates whether the pressure is measured above a vacuum or above the ambient pressure. In either case the unit is the lb per sq in.; the terms absolute and gage do not serve to distinguish the units but only serve to distinguish the concepts. A less confusing nomenclature would be to say that the absolute pressure, or alternatively the gage pressure, is so many lb per sq in.

Concept labels are common where the same unit is used to describe several different concepts. They often provide a convenient shorthand; but unless their role is recognized, they can introduce confusion into the meaning of units.

Sometimes one encounters the reverse of the situation described: the unit is concealed in the description of the concept. A familiar example is the description of the density of a liquid in terms of specific gravity. One commonly states the specific gravity as a number without a unit attached. The rational interpretation of such a description, however, is that a unit equal to the density of water at a specified temperature (and standard atmospheric pressure) is implied. One may argue that specific gravity is just a ratio of two densities and therefore needs no unit; however, one may with equal force argue that length in feet, for example, is merely a ratio of two lengths—the length in question and the length of a standard foot—and also needs no unit. To be consistent, therefore, we must properly regard any variable that is defined as a ratio of one physical variable to another arbitrarily selected variable as denoting a substantial variable defined in terms of the unit that forms the denominator of the ratio.

2-6   Natural Units

We may make a distinction between substantial and natural units similar to the one that we have made between substantial and natural physical variables. A substantial unit is one whose meaning rests on an arbitrary physical standard; a natural unit is one whose meaning is independent of any such standard.

It may seem pointless to make this distinction anew for units. The unit of a substantial variable is a substantial unit, the unit of a natural variable is a natural unit, and that should be that. It happens, however, that the unit is really the key to the nature of the variable, rather than the other way round. Mass or length or time—any of the variables that we normally think of as substantial—may in fact be either substantial or natural depending on the nature of the units in which they are expressed.

The significance of looking at the distinction between the substantial and the natural variable from the point of view of the unit rather than the variable itself will be evident from an example. The length of a 1-inch pipe might be expressed as 10 feet, or it might be expressed as 120 diameters. The first unit (the foot) is a substantial unit and identifies a substantial variable. The second unit (the diameter) is a natural unit, however, and identifies a natural variable. To say that the pipe is 120 diameters long is equivalent to saying that the ratio of pipe length to diameter is 120, which is clearly a natural description. Even though we seem to be talking about a substantial variable, the description we have provided is natural.

The interpretation of the diameter as a natural unit is slightly arbitrary but conceptually sound. One might argue that the diameter is simply an arbitrary standard which rests eventually on some primary standard such as the foot; however, it would clearly be fatuous to use the diameter as a unit if the absolute length were the object of the description. Any time a natural unit of this sort is used, the description accomplished is of a natural variable, even though the language of the description may suggest that a substantial variable is described. Other familiar examples of normally substantial variables being rendered natural by description in terms of natural units are arc length expressed in degrees or radians and head loss in a pipe flow expressed in velocity heads.

2-7 The Physical Relationship among Units

Many units are defined by reference to other units. The unit of area is commonly defined as the area of a square having a side of unit length, the unit of velocity is commonly defined as the velocity that will give a travel of one unit of length during one unit of time, and so on. We find that a whole system of units may be established by reference to only a very few physical standards.

Conventionally we regard certain units as fundamental and the remainder as derived. Since the units of area, volume, velocity, and acceleration may be simply derived from units of length and time, it is customary to regard the former as derived units and the latter as fundamental. Similarly units of work or energy, torque, stress, viscosity, and mass may be derived by defining a unit of force in addition to units of length and time, which suggests that force might appropriately be added to the list of fundamental units. Certain other units—in particular the units of concepts such as specific volume that are related to mass—are more conveniently derived from units of mass, length, and time, however, suggesting that mass has equal claim to being regarded as fundamental. By convention either force, length, and time or mass, length, and time are regarded as the fundamental units of mechanics. Normally the derived units are related to one or the other of these fundamental sets, depending on which is appropriate.

To define the units of thermodynamics or heat transfer, an additional fundamental unit is used beyond the three of mechanics. The conventional selection is temperature. Some also regard the unit of heat as fundamental, but this view is labeled unconventional; the usual view is that the unit of heat properly derives from the unit of work—and therefore from the units of force and length.

The conventions as regards the units of electricity are not so clear. The prevalent view is that the fundamental units of electricity may properly be regarded as being made up of the fundamental units of mechanics plus one electrical unit, the unit of electrical charge being a reasonable choice for the latter unit. The remaining electrical units may then be defined in terms of this fundamental set. This viewpoint is hardly universal, however; some prefer to regard the unit of charge as a derived unit—definable in terms of force and length—which then reduces the list of fundamental units to three.

Both the number and the kind of units we choose to regard as fundamental are arbitrary. The usual criterion is that a derived unit should be related to its parents through some fundamental physical equation, but this notion clearly leaves room for opinion—not only as to what equations are fundamental, but also as to which of the fundamental equations should be put to this use. It is generally agreed, however, that any derivation that depends on the properties of a particular substance does not properly establish a derived unit. As an example, the imperial gallon of Britain is defined as the volume of 10 pounds of water at 62°F. Despite the possibility of defining volume in this manner, however, we do not regard the unit of volume to be derived from the unit of mass. Regardless of its legal definition, in practice we normally consider the imperial gallon—like any other volume unit—to be definable in terms of a unit of length.

Part of the confusion surrounding electrical units arises from a disagreement over the role of Coulomb's law in their definition. Since the unit of electrical charge was originally defined in terms of the force between charges in free space, it is pardonable to regard the unit of charge to be a derived unit. Against this view, however, may be raised the objection that—analogous to the definition of the gallon in terms of the pound—the definition of charge in terms of a free-space relationship involves specification of a special substance (or lack of substance) as a medium. While the decision may be recognized as largely arbitrary, the prevailing view today is that the unit of charge should not properly be regarded as a unit derived from units of force and length.

These remarks, at this point, may seem almost purely pedantic. The agreement as to what units may properly be derived from others, however, has an important bearing on how we treat units mathematically. As the next chapter reveals, the mathematical relationships we establish between units reflect the notions we have of what constitutes a proper derivation of units. The only demand of the mathematics, however, is that some decision be made; propriety is not a mathematical issue. We therefore must seek the decision by other means; and the notion of what constitutes a properly derived unit is the best means we have available. We shall find eventually that the basis for our notion of propriety is somewhat firmer than the present remarks might suggest.

Problems and Examples

2-1. The visual brightness of stars is often described by a variable known as magnitude. A star is said to be one magnitude higher than another if its light is fainter in the ratio 2.512 (the fifth root of 100). Does this scale of values define a unit; and if so, is it a proper unit of brightness?

Solution. From this definition of magnitude it can be seen that it is related to brightness by the equation

$$\frac{b_2}{b_1} = (2.512)^{(m_1 - m_2)},$$

where b is brightness and m is magnitude. This equation establishes magnitude as a continuous function of the physical variable brightness, and therefore as a legitimate physical variable itself. Although one is free to select the datum, the unit of m is established by the equation. The unit, however, is clearly not a unit of brightness, since a unit change in magnitude corresponds to different changes in brightness if the initial brightness (or magnitude) is different.

2-2. If the half tones of the tempered musical scale are given consecutive numbers (for example, middle C = 0, D = 2, E = 4, F = 5, etc.), is a unit definable by reference to this scale of numbers? If so, is it a unit of frequency?

2-3. The kinematic viscosity of liquids is often measured by an instrument known as the Saybolt Universal viscosimeter, which is essentially a container with a small tube in the bottom. The kinematic viscosity may be related to the time taken to drain the container by the following equation (for time between 50 and 100 sec):

$$\nu = 0.220t - \frac{195}{t},$$

where ν is kinematic viscosity in centistokes and t is time in seconds.

a. Is a unit of kinematic viscosity defined by the Saybolt Universal time scale?

b. Which of the following conventional descriptions (if either) would be consistent with the normal mode of physical description? (1) The viscosity is 60 SSU (seconds Saybolt Universal). (2) The Saybolt Universal viscosity is 60 sec. Explain.

2-4. In the following statements identify the concepts and the units involved:

a. A temperature of 60°F is equivalent to 520°R.

b. A standard atmosphere corresponds to 14.7 lb per sq in. abs.

c. The acceleration is 5 g's.

d. Chlorine has an atomic weight of 35.5.

e. The velocity is three times the ambient speed of sound.

2-5. The universal gas constant may be expressed as

$$R = 83.15 \cdot 10^6 \text{ ergs per g mole per } °K.$$

The gram mole occurring in the unit of this constant is often defined as a unit of mass equal to the molecular weight expressed in grams.

On the other hand, the gas constant for a single molecule (Boltzmann's constant) is usually expressed as

$$k = 1.3802 \cdot 10^{-16} \text{ erg per } °K.$$

How, if at all, are the units of these quantities related?

Solution. Superficially it would appear that the two units describe quite different concepts, since one involves mass and the other doesn't. A more appropriate interpretation, however, is that the gram mole is not a unit of mass but rather a unit of molecular population. Specifically the gram mole equals $6.021 \cdot 10^{23}$ molecules (Avogadro's number). With this interpretation the two constants could be expressed as

$R = 83.15 \cdot 10^6$ ergs per $6.021 \cdot 10^{23}$ molecules per $°K$,
$k = 1.3802 \cdot 10^{-16}$ ergs per molecule per $°K$,

which shows them to be directly analogous concepts differing only in being referred to a different number of molecules. Some writers specify the units as being simply ergs per $°K$ (or ft-lb per $°R$ in British units) for either concept.

The gram mole can be regarded as a natural unit of mass which does not define the mass absolutely but defines it by reference to the mass of the molecules involved. To express the mass in gram moles is equivalent to dividing the mass in grams by the mass of a molecule in atomic mass units (mass unit = one-six-teenth the mass of oxygen 16). The concept described is therefore not mass but a natural concept proportional to the number of molecules.

3

The Mathematical
Nature of Units

3-1 Introduction

Although the original reason for defining units was
probably for the sake of duplicating physical magnitudes, a more significant benefit of the notion is that
it permits physical variables to be treated mathematically. The application of mathematics to such variables is so familiar that it is easy to imagine that it is
an entirely natural maneuver; but closer inspection
reveals that the translation from physical reality to
mathematical abstraction may proceed along several
alternative routes. Just how the physical idea of a
physical variable or its unit translates into the language
of mathematics is therefore a question that deserves
careful study.

3-2 The Mathematical Interpretation
of Physical Variables

There are two somewhat discordant interpretations
of the role of units in the mathematical description of

24

physical variables. One view is that the unit is an integral part of the physical definition of the variable; the other view is that the unit is an integral part of the mathematical description of the variable. As an example, proponents of the first viewpoint would argue that, when one says a length is 10 ft, the foot label is not properly regarded as a part of the mathematical description; more properly one should probably say that the length in feet is 10, since the length in feet is the physical variable described and 10 is its mathematical description. The opposing viewpoint is that the concept described is length, rather than length in feet, and that its mathematical description is 10 ft—that is, 10 times ft—not just 10; in other words, a physical variable may properly be defined without reference to a specific unit and may be represented mathematically by a number times a unit.

The first interpretation has the advantage of being linguistically sound. Designating the foot as the unit of length should be tantamount to identifying the foot mathematically with unity; if the foot is mathematically unity, 10 ft is mathematically 10. Very little imagination is needed, however, to recognize that such a scheme has its awkward features. If we adopt this view, we may not, for example, write an equation such as

$$L = 10 \text{ ft} = 3.05 \text{ meters,} \qquad (3\text{-}1)$$

for both the foot and the meter lay equal claim to a value of 1. If we never cared to change units, nor cared what would happen if we did, this interpretation would probably be entirely satisfactory. But we are often confronted with the practical necessity of changing units; and even though the practical necessity may be avoided, or met by rule of thumb, we still have a theoretical interest in the operation. By defining the physical variable in such a way that it changes every time we change units, we make the analysis of the effect of a unit change more difficult.

If we adopt the alternative approach of regarding the physical variable as the product of the number times the unit, we succeed in defining a concept that is invariant with respect to change in size of unit. A length of 10 ft or of 3.05 meters is then not only physically the same length but is also mathematically the same variable: a change from feet to meters changes the number and the unit, but not the physical variable. The full advantage of such a description may not be superficially obvious, but one may recall that in any investigation of the effect of a transformation the question of what remains unchanged is usually basic: the invariants are the key to the transformation. Since the physical variable defined as the product of a number and a unit is the invariant as far as a transformation of units is concerned, the aptness of this interpretation may reasonably be anticipated.

Before this notion of a physical variable is accepted, however, one may justifiably 'desire more assurance that a unit can be regarded as a mathematical entity. The notion that a physical magnitude may always be represented by the reduplication or subdivision of a unit strongly suggests the mathematical nature of a unit; but both the notion itself and the suggestion it provides are perhaps not unassailable. We may gain assurance of the mathematical nature of the unit, however, if we consider the possibility of defining what we shall call an ultimate unit. We shall assume that it is possible to establish a special unit that can be assigned a value of unity: that is, we shall accept the first notion of a physical variable as valid for this particular unit— but only for this unit. In terms of the ultimate unit, the physical variable that we define will be a pure number; furthermore, the units that we normally use may also be represented as pure numbers by reference to this ultimate unit. With this ultimate unit as a reference, therefore, a physical variable defined as a number times a unit may be recognized as ultimately representing a product of two numbers. The only question remaining is whether a unit has the property of being described in terms of some ultimate unit by a single number—but in the final analysis this is just what we mean by a unit; the physical conclusions of the last chapter can be summed up mathematically merely by saying that a unit has this property.

We of course avoid identifying the ultimate unit with any particular unit in use. As soon as we described a physical variable in terms of the ultimate unit we would lose the flexibility we are seeking to preserve. But by adopting this notion of an ultimate unit we are able to explain many of the properties of units that might otherwise seem strange or even questionable.

3-3 The Mathematical Relationship among Units

The idea that units can be regarded mathematically as numbers of varying sizes suggests the possibility of writing equations between them that reflect their physical relationship. The mathematical relationship between units of the same physical variable arises in an obvious manner; the mere notion of an ultimate unit at once gives meaning to an equation such as

$$1 \text{ ft} = 0.305 \text{ m}. \tag{3-2}$$

The meaning of a relationship between unlike units, however, is not so easily established.

To establish how unlike units are related, it is necessary to look at how the relationship between physical variables is expressed mathematically. Unless we presume a relationship among units at the outset, the only way we have available for setting up a relationship among physical variables is to set up a relationship among the numbers that are used to describe them. A mathematical description of this sort, which treats directly the physical variables stripped of their units, is commonly termed a numerical equation.

As an example of a numerical equation, we might write the relationship between velocity, distance, and time (for uniform motion) as

$$V' = \frac{s'}{t'}. \tag{3-3}$$

If the units used for distance and time are the foot and the second, the parameters V', s', and t' are related to the physical variables V, s, and t by the equations

$$V = V' \text{ ft per sec}, \tag{3-4}$$
$$s = s' \text{ ft}, \tag{3-5}$$
$$t = t' \text{ sec}. \tag{3-6}$$

The name of the velocity unit (foot per second) comes about from a recognition that the velocity describes the number of feet traveled during a second.

By convention the form of Eq. (3-3) is accepted as standard. We could write any number of equations for velocity that do not take this form, but we would regard them as nonstandard. For example, the numerical equation

$$V' = 60 \frac{s'}{t'} \tag{3-7}$$

is an entirely legitimate equation for velocity if velocity is expressed in ft per min rather than ft per sec (with the units of s and t as before). But we do not regard this equation as standard. The distinguishing feature of a standard equation is that it jibes with the standard physical definition of the concept involved. Velocity is normally defined as the distance traveled per unit of time; therefore, a travel of one unit during a time of one unit should give a velocity of one unit. Equation (3-3) gives velocity in a unit that is consistent with this notion; Eq. (3-7) doesn't. Admittedly we obtain just as proper a description of velocity from Eq. (3-7), but the description is inconsistent with the descriptions we have used for length and time. Units that conform with the accepted standard forms of the equations that relate physical concepts—or with the accepted physical definitions of the concepts—are commonly called consistent units. Although Eq. (3-3) was written to accommodate the foot per second, the foot, and the second, it will of course accommodate any other consistent units.

The sizes of consistent units are clearly interdependent. Should the size of the foot or the second change, the size of the foot per second would also have to change to preserve the standard relationship between V', s', and t'. The implied mathematical relationship between the units may easily be formulated by a consideration of ultimate units. If we specify that the numbers obtained by expressing the variables in terms of the ultimate units are related in the same way as v', s', and t'—in other words, if we assume that the ultimate units are consistent—then we may relate these variables (which we designate by double primes) as

$$V'' = \frac{s''}{t''}. \qquad (3\text{-}8)$$

Since these variables are mathematically identical to the physical variables V, s, and t of Eqs. (3-4) to (3-6), we see that

$$\text{ft per sec} = \frac{V''}{V'}, \tag{3-9}$$

$$\text{ft} = \frac{s''}{s'}, \tag{3-10}$$

$$\sec = \frac{t''}{t'}. \tag{3-11}$$

These equations define the numbers that may be assigned to the units if they are expressed in terms of the ultimate units. A combination of these three equations with Eqs. (3-3) and (3-8) then gives a direct relationship between the units:

$$\text{ft per sec} = \text{ft/sec.} \tag{3-12}$$

This result probably seems obvious; however, what makes it obvious should probably be interpreted as a fortuitous accident of nomenclature. Instead of conceiving of velocity as the distance traveled per unit of time, we might have conceived of it—with perhaps some stretch of the imagination—as the inverse of the time taken to travel a unit distance. Conceiving of velocity in this manner, we would probably give the unit of inverse time a label such as the inverse second and call the velocity unit the inverse second per foot. The identification of this unit with the ft/sec would then not be obvious.

Another simple example will more clearly demonstrate the arbitrary nature of the relationships that we erect between units. We may describe the area of a square by the following numerical equation:

$$A' = s'^2. \tag{3-13}$$

The numbers here may be related to the physical area A and the physical length of a side s by the equations

$$A = A' \text{ sq ft}, \tag{3-14}$$

$$s = s' \text{ ft}. \tag{3-15}$$

If we argue that the variables as described in terms of ultimate units are also related by an equation of the form of Eq. (3-13), we come up with the familiar relationship

$$\text{sq ft} = \text{ft}^2. \tag{3-16}$$

The idea of area, and its unit, however, may be conceived in many different ways. An equation of exactly the form of Eq. (3-13) may be written for the area of a circle:

$$A' = D'^2. \tag{3-17}$$

This is the proper numerical equation if the unit of length is the foot and the unit of area is the circular foot (the area of a unit circle) rather than the square foot (the area of a unit square). The parameters of Eq. (3-17) are related to the area A and the diameter D by the equations

$$A = A' \text{ cir ft}, \tag{3-18}$$
$$D = D' \text{ ft}. \tag{3-19}$$

If we now argued as before, we would be led to identify the circular foot with the ft^2. The ultimate units, however, may not be consistent with both Eq. (3-13) and Eq. (3-17): a choice must be made. We choose of course to regard the equation we have written for the area of the square to be standard and use it to define the ultimate units. We therefore accept Eq. (3-16) as the proper relationship between the units of area and length (and along with it the linguistic requirement, and ft^2 is read "foot squared" rather than "foot circled").

We see from this demonstration that the relationships among units are not wholly automatic. How the units are related is dependent on an agreement as to the form the pertinent equations would take if the variables were expressed in terms of ultimate units. Clearly, in terms of ultimate units the equation for the area of a square may take only one form; and if this form is specified, the equation for the area of a circle may not also be specified. What we choose to specify and how we choose to specify it determines how the units are related. Although in some instances the specification follows naturally from the physical notions we have of the concepts, in many instances the specification is almost completely arbitrary.

In at least one instance the form of equation that we specify as standard—hence the basis for defining consistent units—can be regarded as being chosen only in defiance of the conventional physical notions. The standard equation that relates mass to force can hardly be defended as reflecting a conventional view of mass. The popular conception of mass is in terms of the force exerted by standard gravity. The seemingly natural way to relate force to mass is therefore by an equation that would take the form

$$F' = m' \frac{a'}{g'_o}. \tag{3-20}$$

If the foot, second, and pound are used as units, the variables in this equation are related to the physical variables by the equations

$$F \text{ (force)} = F' \text{ lb}_f, \tag{3-21}$$
$$m \text{ (mass)} = m' \text{ lb}_m, \tag{3-22}$$
$$a \text{ (acceleration)} = a' \text{ ft/sec}^2, \tag{3-23}$$
$$g_o \text{ (std accel. of grav.)} = g'_o \text{ ft/sec}^2. \tag{3-24}$$

The subscripts on the pound units are necessary because they are not yet identified as the same unit. This equation gives the reasonable conclusion that if a mass is subjected to the standard acceleration of gravity the force acting on it will be just equal to the mass. If we regarded this as the standard equation, we would then be led to the logical conclusion that the force-pound

(lb_f) and the mass-pound (lb_m) are identical units, as their names so strongly suggest.

We do not make this choice, however. Instead the simpler relation

$$F' = m'a' \qquad (3\text{-}25)$$

is regarded as the standard form of the equation and is used to define consistent units and the relationship among them. As a consequence of this choice we are forced to the conclusion that the lb_m and the lb_f are not the same unit in spite of their intimate physical connection but are related by the equation

$$lb_f = g'_o \ lb_m ft/sec^2, \qquad (3\text{-}26)$$

which might alternatively be written

$$lb_f = g_o \ lb_m. \qquad (3\text{-}27)$$

For reasons that we shall discuss later (Chap. 8), this choice of a standard equation is commendable; but the benefits of such a selection are gained at the price of denying the identity of two units that have for honest reasons even earned the same name.

In the final analysis, the direct effect of agreeing to regard certain equations as standard, and therefore a basis for defining ultimate units, is to establish an equality between units where only a proportionality existed before. If we do not elect to give the accolade to any particular form of equation, we could say only the following about the units we have considered:

$$ft \ per \ sec \sim ft/sec, \qquad (3\text{-}28)$$
$$sq \ ft \sim ft^2, \qquad (3\text{-}29)$$
$$cir \ ft \sim ft^2, \qquad (3\text{-}30)$$
$$lb_f \sim lb_m. \qquad (3\text{-}31)$$

By introducing the idea of standard equations for defining the various physical concepts—or standard physical situations for establishing the relationships among ultimate units—we merely replace the proportionalities by equations (which involve appropriate proportionality factors):

$$\text{ft per sec} = \text{ft/sec}, \tag{3-32}$$

$$\text{sq ft} = \text{ft}^2, \tag{3-33}$$

$$\text{cir ft} = \frac{\pi}{4} \text{ft}^2, \tag{3-34}$$

$$\text{lb}_f = g_o \text{ lb}_m. \tag{3-35}$$

Although it may be contended without much fear of dispute that there is no theoretical necessity of setting up such equations between units, it may also be contended that there is considerable desirability—both theoretical and practical—in such a move. One conspicuous advantage is that it permits the equations that relate physical variables to be written directly in terms of physical variables—that is, as "physical equations."

3-4 Physical Equations

The arguments of the preceding section lead immediately to the notion that equations may be written that involve the physical variables directly. By virtue of our definition of ultimate units, the numbers that we would get by expressing the physical variable in terms of ultimate units are synonymous with the physical variables themselves. Therefore, when we agree to establish a relationship among these numbers, we at the same time establish a relationship among the physical variables. Specifically, the relationship established by Eq. (3-8) may equally well be written

$$V = \frac{s}{t}, \tag{3-36}$$

in which the symbols represent numbers times units. To arrive at the equation from a somewhat different direction, we might combine Eqs. (3-3) and (3-12) to get

$$V' \text{ ft per sec } = \frac{s' \text{ ft}}{t' \text{ sec}}, \qquad (3\text{-}37)$$

which reduces to Eq. (3-36) by virtue of Eqs. (3-4) to (3-6). An equation that involves the physical variables directly is commonly called a physical equation.

The practical advantage of the physical equation is that the whole story is in the equation. No units need to be specified because they come out automatically: if one substitutes s in feet and t in seconds into Eq. (3-36), one gets V in feet/second simply by obeying the mathematics.

Beyond this obvious advantage the physical equation has some subtler advantages. A particular physical fact is described by only one physical equation involving a single set of variables, independent of what units may be employed. In other words, the physical equation, like the physical variable, is invariant with respect to changes in units. This property—we shall find—makes it much easier to express certain generalizations about physical relations than would otherwise be possible.

Though we restrained ourselves from doing it, we could alternatively have arrived at the notion of physical equations without first laboring through a discussion of numerical equations. Once we accept the notion that a physical variable formed as the product of a number and a unit represents an invariant mathematical notion expressible as a pure number in terms of some arbitrarily selected ultimate unit, it is apparent that we are free to use these variables at once in describing physical relationships. The way in which the relationships are formed determines the full meaning of the variables and at the same time establishes the relationship between the units in which they may be expressed. Thus we might say at the outset that we shall define velocity by the physical equation

$$V = \frac{s}{t}. \tag{3-38}$$

From this equation we find at once that, if the foot is used to define length and the second to define time, then velocity automatically earns a meaning (the distance traveled per second) and a unit (the foot/second). To justify this starting point, we need merely argue that the only result of our action is the implicit establishment of a permissible relationship between the ultimate units. We are of course at liberty to give the unit so defined a new name, though we are also at liberty to leave it with just the name given to it by its parents. Although the approach suggested by these remarks is sound, its implications are perhaps too well concealed. Once one recognizes the full meaning of a relationship between physical variables, however, there is no reason why such relationships may not be established directly.

3-5 The Units of Natural Variables

Perhaps the most important consequence of establishing mathematical relationships among units is that it gives to any natural variable a unit that can be identified as a specific number. In this way the fact that the evaluation of a natural variable does not depend on an arbitrary physical standard can be recognized very easily. As a simple example, the humidity of air is often expressed in terms of the grains of water vapor per pound of air. From a mathematical interpretation of units we are able to recognize that the unit of grains per pound reduces to gr per lb $= $ gr/lb $=$ gr/7,000 gr $= 1/7,000.$ (3-39)

We are therefore able to identify the unit as being independent of any particular physical standard and to conclude that the variable is a natural variable.

If the natural variable involves substantial variables of the same sort, its identification is easy by any route; however, if it involves a collection of dissimilar concepts, the recognition may not be so easy. It would be rather a chore, for example, to establish Reynolds number as a natural variable if we did not admit mathematical relationships among the units involved in its calculation. But if we treat these units mathematically, we may easily demonstrate that its unit is a definite pure number. Should we use lb_m/ft^3 for density, ft/sec for velocity, ft for length, and $lb_m/sec\text{-}ft$ for viscosity, we would find immediately that the unit of a Reynolds number so evaluated is unity, since

$$\frac{lb_m}{ft^3} \cdot \frac{ft}{sec} \cdot ft \cdot \frac{sec\text{-}ft}{lb_m} = 1. \qquad (3\text{-}40)$$

Any other combination of units can similarly be identified with a pure number if appropriate recognition of the interrelation among units is made. As another example, if the same units are used for density, velocity, and length, but $lb_f sec/ft^2$ is used for viscosity, Reynolds number comes out with the unit $lb_m ft/lb_f sec^2$. Recognition of the relation between the lb_f and the lb_m [Eq. (3-26)] establishes this unit as equal to $1/g_o'$, or $1/32.174$.

One may perhaps detect a tinge of arbitrariness in the suggestion that the unit of a natural variable is always a definite pure number. It is clear, for example, that Reynolds number should not directly owe its naturalness to the chance circumstance that we have erected a relationship between units of force and mass. Had we chosen some other relationship to define mass or force, Reynolds number should still be natural; however, its unit would not appear to be identifiable with a constant. In such a circumstance, however, we would normally introduce an appropriate factor into the definition of Reynolds number to make its unit still come out as a constant. In other words, the fact that the unit of a natural variable may be identified as a constant is partly the result of a convention. That we may always define natural variables in this way will be evident from an example. Newton's law of gravitation states that the force attracting two masses is proportional to the product of the masses and to the inverse square of their separation, or

$$F = G \frac{m_1 m_2}{r^2}, \qquad (3\text{-}41)$$

where G is an appropriate factor of proportionality. In a situation where this law could be assumed to be pertinent, we could easily argue that a variable such as Fr^2/m^2 is a natural variable. By defining a unit of force equal to the force exerted by two unit masses a unit distance apart, we could even show that Fr^2/m^2 can be given a unit of unity. By any conventional relationship among units, however, the identification of the unit of Fr^2/m^2 as a constant is impossible. We may easily rectify this situation by the simple introduction of G into the natural variable. The variable Fr^2/Gm^2 will then have a unit of unity if G is given the units called for by a physical interpretation of Eq. (3-41). By similar arguments, if we had chosen to use Eq. (3-20) to define the relationship between consistent force and mass units, we would not write Reynolds number as $\rho V D/\mu$, but rather as $\rho V D/\mu g_o$.

As a consequence of our conventions, if consistent units are used to describe the substantial variables that go to define a natural variable, the unit of the natural variable will normally be unity. To put it another way, any consistent unit of a natural variable is equal to its ultimate unit—that is, to unity. Most natural variables are defined for consistent units; and since this gives to their unit a value of unity, no unit label is needed. Despite the mathematical lack of necessity, however, certain natural units that may be identified with unity are still labeled: the presence of a label is no assurance that the unit is not unity.

The circumstance of a natural unit being equal to unity, yet still meriting a label, is encountered in the description of angle. Angles are most easily defined in terms of the arc traced by the extremity of a radius swung through the angle in question. The ratio of the arc length to its radius gives the angle in radians, the ratio of the arc length to its full circumference gives the angle in revolutions, and the ratio of the arc length to $\frac{1}{360}$ of its full circumference gives the angle in degrees. From these three definitions it is apparent that angle is a natural variable; the three different units, therefore, should be identifiable with pure numbers.

Just what numbers the three units correspond to depends on what we accept as the standard definition of angle. By the usual convention the proper physical equation for angle is

$$\alpha = \frac{s}{r}, \tag{3-42}$$

where s and r are arc length and radius, respectively. This, of course, is the defining equation for the radian (if s and r are expressed in the same units) and gives to the radian a value of unity: in other words, the radian label is superfluous. Despite its mathematical superfluity, however, the radian label is usually retained in describing angle to avoid confusion with the degree or revolution (unless the angle is quoted as a fraction or multiple of π).

In many respects the revolution would have been a more satisfactory choice as the consistent unit of angle. The fact that the radian was selected instead is sometimes got round by defining a new concept, the rotation, for which the consistent unit—the unit that can be identified with unity—is the revolution. In more familiar terms this invention gives rise to the notion of rotative speed, with a consistent unit of revolutions per unit time. A physical equation that called for rotative speed would then presumably be appropriate for a unit such as revolutions/second (which would reduce to $\sec^{-1}$), whereas an equation that called for angular speed would be appropriate for a unit such as radians/second (which, in the different context, would also reduce to $\sec^{-1}$). Since angle may be used to describe rotation and rotation to describe angle, the chance for confusion is obvious: in describing angle the radian may be identified with unity and the revolution with 2π; in describing rotation the revolution may be identified with unity and the radian with $1/2\pi$. Some argue that there is really only one concept involved and it should therefore be accorded only one consistent unit (presumably the radian); but though the argument has considerable merit, it has apparently not been fully convincing.

A similar distinction is made in treating vibrations and other alternating phenomena. The customary mathematical language of vibrations relates a cycle of motion to one revolution of angle. Angle may therefore serve to describe cyclic frequency in much the way that it serves to describe rotational frequency. One may then speak either of frequency in cycles per unit time or of "circular frequency" in radians per unit time. Again one may argue that two different concepts with two different consistent units are involved; and again one may counter that only one concept is really involved and only one unit (the same unit as used for rotative or angular speed) should be regarded as consistent.

3-6   The Meaning of Dimensions

The relationships that are set up among units have an important side effect. When we identify the square foot with the foot squared, for example, we do more than merely introduce a notion that makes the conversion of units simpler; we also reveal a good deal about how the physical concepts of length and area are related. To take full advantage of this aspect of units, the idea of dimensions has been introduced. At this point it is not possible to reveal the full significance of dimensions; however, they are closely analogous to units in nature if not in purpose and therefore are appropriately discussed along with them.

The simplest viewpoint—though not the only one— is that a dimension is no more than a generalized unit. Anything that could be measured in length units, for example, is said to have the dimensions of length; anything that could be measured in mass units is said to have the dimensions of mass: in general, the specific unit merely has to be replaced by the general concept to get the dimension.

We freely admit relationships among dimensions analogous to those among consistent units: in effect, we endow dimensions with a universal consistency. For example, instead of saying in seemingly more general fashion that the dimension of velocity is proportional to the dimension of length over the dimension of time, we simply say that velocity has the dimensions of length over time. But since we never associate specific numbers with dimensions, we lose no generality by this presumption of consistency.

Dimensional nomenclature is not entirely consistent. Most writers assign capital letters to basic dimensions: M for mass, F for force, L for length, T for time, etc. Brackets are often used to mean "the dimensions of" (the enclosed variable). As an example of these notations, we would arrive at the dimensions of Reynolds number by the following series of equations:

$$[\rho] = \frac{M}{L^3}, \tag{3-43}$$

$$[V] = \frac{L}{T}, \tag{3-44}$$

$$[D] = L, \tag{3-45}$$

$$[\mu] = \frac{FT}{L^2} = \frac{M}{LT}, \tag{3-46}$$

$$\left[\frac{\rho V D}{\mu}\right] = \frac{M}{L^3} \cdot \frac{L}{T} \cdot L \cdot \frac{LT}{M} = 1. \tag{3-47}$$

The meaning of the first equation is that the dimensions of density are mass over length cubed—and so on. Some writers prefer to regard the symbols on the right-hand sides of these equations as standing for physical variables rather than dimensions and therefore bracket them also; on the other hand one may choose to regard the symbols on the left-hand sides as well as the right-hand as standing for dimensions and leave those brackets off. Fortunately the question of notation is of little importance and seldom if ever a source of confusion in itself.

A variable that is shown to have a dimension of unity

is said to have no dimensions, or to be dimensionless. The usage is perhaps a bit loose but parallels our usual practice of regarding a variable that has a unit of unity as having no units (where we should perhaps more properly say that it needs no unit label). Since any natural variable has a unit of unity if expressed in consistent units, all natural variables are dimensionless variables, or, more popularly, dimensionless numbers. The dimensionless character of Reynolds number is demonstrated by Eq. (3-47).

Although custom has somewhat blunted the distinction, dimensions are unlike units in that their interrelation should properly be based on the situation at hand rather than on the possibly inappropriate conventions that relate units. The basis for such a viewpoint is that dimensions are defined specifically for the sake of identifying natural variables. Since a natural variable is natural only in a specific context, it should properly be regarded as dimensionless only in the same context and not per se. Therefore such notions as considering force to have the dimensions of mass times acceleration should not be considered universal truths, but as relationships appropriate to some situations and inappropriate to others. Reynolds number is a dimensional variable only if we give force the dimensions of mass times acceleration; similarly it is a natural variable only in flows that involve Newton's law: it has no proper place in flows that do not involve Newton's law and strictly speaking has no right to be called dimensionless in such contexts. Although in conventional usage little heed is paid to these notions, it is worth remembering that a dimensionless number is significant only to the extent that the relationships that render it dimensionless are pertinent.

Bowing to conventional usage, we shall adopt the

notion that in any general context the dimensions of a variable are the dimensions given to it by acceptance of the conventional relationships among units. The conventional dimensions so defined provide a handy scheme for describing in a general way how units are conventionally related; they are also of utility in many physical situations for identifying natural variables. These conventional dimensions, as well as the conventional dimensionless numbers definable from them, are therefore useful concepts. As we shall find, however, they are somewhat special concepts.

The idea that a dimension represents a generalized unit is not the only possible interpretation of the term. Some prefer to regard a dimension as designating the number that is used in describing a physical variable, rather than the unit. With this interpretation, if one says that velocity has the dimensions of length over time, one means that the number that describes a velocity in a particular situation may be equated to some number describing length divided by some number describing time. Since the particular physical variables one is referring to can't be identified except as a class, the notion is necessarily vague until one sees what use it is put to. The notion does, however, somewhat explain how the term dimension came to be used in the present context and probably can justifiably boast historical support. But in spite of arguments that may be raised in support of such a viewpoint—in which one may detect reflections of the same objections that are raised against treating units mathematically—the idea of regarding dimensions as units of a special sort gives to dimensions a more easily comprehended meaning and results in exactly the same final conclusions. Confusing the picture still more is the idea held by some that the term dimension properly refers to the exponent in a dimensional formula. With this usage one would say that velocity has dimensions of 1 in length and −1 in time. With this interpretation a dimensionless number can be called dimensionless without apology; however, this would seem to be small justification for an otherwise awkward terminology. One might reasonably argue that different terms should be used for these various interpretations; but since the same relations obtain no matter what interpretation is made, it is quite natural that the same term is retained. It is quite possible that the argument between the conflicting viewpoints is more semantic than philosophical. But whatever the proper conclusion of the argument, the more common interpretation of the meaning of dimension is probably in terms of units—though many writers succeed in defining dimensions so vaguely that any interpretation will fit.

Problems and Examples

3-1. Comment on the following equation:

$$p = 20 \text{ lb/in.}^2 \text{ gage} = 34.7 \text{ lb/in.}^2 \text{ abs.}$$

Solution. Since the two units are the same size, this equation says that $20 = 34.7$ and is clearly not mathematically correct. We frequently use an equals sign to mean "transforms to"; in such usage, the sign cannot be given its normal mathematical meaning.

3-2. Which of the following equations are mathematically proper?

a. 100 SSU = 20 centistokes,
b. 1 ft²/sec = 929 stokes,
c. 60°F = 520°R,
d. 15°C = 59°F,
e. 273°K = 492°R.

3-3. If the electrical conductance of a wire 1,000 ft

long is 0.5 mho, what is the conductance per foot? What is the relationship between the mho per foot, the mho, and the foot?

3-4. The electrical resistivity of standard annealed copper at 20°C is 0.6788 microhm per inch cube and the electrical conductivity 1.473 megamhos per inch cube. What are the units of these variables in terms of the microhm or megamho and the inch?

3-5. What familiar concepts may be expressed in the following units, and what is the relationship between the units listed and the more familiar forms, if the latter are expressed in terms of the pound, foot, and second?

  a. $lb_m ft/sec^2$,
  b. $lb_f sec^2/ft^4$,
  c. Btu/lb_f,
  d. $(Btu/lb_m)^{1/2}$.

3-6. The force between two electrical charges may be described most simply by the equation

$$F = \frac{q_1 q_2}{\epsilon r^2},$$

where F = force,
     q_1, q_2 = charge strengths,
      r = their separation,
      ϵ = permittivity of medium.

For the sake of simplifying other electrical equations, however, a more complicated form of this equation is also in use:

$$F = \frac{q_1 q_2}{4\pi \epsilon r^2}.$$

For F in dynes, r in centimeters, and q in statcoulombs, determine the following (the statcoulomb is defined as the charge that would exert a force of one dyne on a similar charge one centimeter away in free space):

a. If each equation in turn is considered to be a physical equation, what are the respective units of permittivity in terms of the dyne, centimeter, and statcoulomb?

b. In each of these units, what is the permittivity of free space?

Solution. *a.* In either case the unit of permittivity would be identified as the $(statcoulomb)^2/dyne\text{-}cm^2$. Using the facts that the statfarad is equal to a statcoulomb/statvolt and a statvolt is equal to a dyne-cm/statcoulomb, this unit may be more simply expressed as the statfarad/cm.

b. Substituting unit values of force, charge, and distance into the two equations, we find that the first gives a free-space value of ϵ of 1 statfarad/cm and the second of $1/4\pi$ statfarad/cm. The latter value is normally considered proper: in other words, the latter equation is the one considered to be the proper physical equation. The former equation is then properly regarded as a numerical equation calling for a unit of $1/4\pi$ statfarad/cm (that is, the permittivity of free space) for ϵ.

3-7. *a.* If the following equations are interpreted as physical equations, what are the units of μ and ν in terms of lb_f, ft, and sec and in terms of lb_m, ft, and sec? How are the alternative units related?

$$\tau = \mu \frac{dV}{dy}, \qquad \nu = \frac{\mu}{\rho},$$

where τ = shear stress,
  V = velocity,
  y = distance,
  μ = (absolute) viscosity,
  ν = kinematic viscosity,
  ρ = density.

b. What would be the answers to these questions if the following equations were regarded as physical?

$$\tau = \frac{\mu}{g_o}\frac{dV}{dy}, \qquad \nu = \frac{\mu}{\rho},$$

where g_o is the standard acceleration of gravity.

c. What would be the answer to parts *a* and *b* if the following equation were regarded as the physical equation relating force, mass, and acceleration?

$$F = m\frac{a}{g_o}.$$

3-8. Determine the magnitude of the following natural variables in terms of the indicated units, determine the numerical magnitude of the resulting units, and determine the magnitude of the natural variables in consistent units:

a. Mach number (V/c) for $V = 1,100$ mph and $c = 1,100$ ft/sec.

b. Heat rate (WH/P) for $W = 100,000$ lb/hr, $H = 1,000$ Btu/lb, $P = 10,000$ kw.

c. Reynolds number $(\rho VD/\mu)$ for $\rho = 50$ lb/ft^3, $V = 100$ ft/sec, $D = 5$ ft, $\mu = 0.00005$ lb-sec/ft^2.

3-9. If force, length, time, and charge $(F, L, T,$ and $Q)$ are considered the fundamental dimensions of electricity, what are the dimensions of the following variables?

a. Charge.

b. Current (charge per unit time).

c. Voltage (work per unit charge).

d. Impedance (voltage per unit current).

e. Capacitance (charge per unit voltage).

3-10. If permittivity is considered a natural variable, determine the dimensions of the variables of Prob. 3-9 in terms of force, length, and time (see Prob. 3-6 for definition of permittivity).

3-11. If the dimensions of density, velocity, and length are considered fundamental, what are the dimensions of pressure, viscosity, power?

3-12. If energy is considered to have the dimensions of mass, what are the dimensions of velocity and time in terms of mass and length?

3-13. If Newton's law of gravitation rather than his law of motion is used to establish the relationship between force and mass dimensions, what are the dimensions of Reynolds number in terms of M, L, and T?

4

Problems of Conversion

4-1 Introduction

In dealing with physical variables and the equations that involve them one is frequently confronted with problems or instances of conversion. Not only is there the obvious problem of converting the units of physical variables, there are also problems of converting equations so that they will handle different units or even different concepts. The function of this chapter is to demonstrate how an understanding of how units and concepts are related solves such problems.

4-2 The Conversion of Units

The ordinary conversion of units seems simple enough; but one can get into trouble occasionally unless one proceeds in a mathematically proper manner. The technique that is generally simplest and has gained most favor is to multiply the number to be converted by appropriate dimensionless conversion factors formed as ratios of equivalent magnitudes. As an example, to convert 10 ft to inches, one would write

$$10 \text{ ft} = 10 \text{ ft} \left(\frac{12 \text{ in.}}{\text{ft}} \right) = 120 \text{ in.} \qquad (4\text{-}1)$$

In this equation the units match throughout and are easily checked. The operation is equivalent to multiplying by unity, so that 10 ft and 120 in. must be identical concepts: in fact, conversion factors are sometimes called unity factors. As a more complicated example, 1 hp could be converted to watts as follows:

$$1 \text{ hp} = 1 \text{ hp} \left(\frac{550 \text{ ft-lb}_f}{\text{hp-sec}}\right) \left(\frac{1{,}000 \text{ g}_f}{2.20 \text{ lb}_f}\right) \left(\frac{981 \text{ dynes}}{\text{g}_f}\right)$$

$$\left(\frac{12 \text{ in.}}{\text{ft}}\right) \left(\frac{2.54 \text{ cm}}{\text{in.}}\right)$$

$$= \frac{550 \cdot 10^3 \cdot 981 \cdot 12 \cdot 2.54}{2.20} \frac{\text{dyne-cm}}{\text{sec}}$$

$$= 746 \cdot 10^7 \frac{\text{dyne-cm}}{\text{sec}} \left(\frac{\text{ergs}}{\text{dyne-cm}}\right) \left(\frac{\text{joules}}{10^7 \text{ ergs}}\right)$$

$$\left(\frac{\text{watt-sec}}{\text{joules}}\right)$$

$$= 746 \text{ watts.} \tag{4-2}$$

The same result can, of course, be obtained by direct unit substitution, but the technique is likely to be more long-winded and harder to check. The conversion of Eq. (4-2), for example, could be carried out as follows:

$$1 \text{ hp} = 550 \frac{\text{ft-lb}_f}{\text{sec}} = 550 \frac{\text{ft}}{\text{sec}} \left(\frac{1}{2.20} \text{ kg}_f\right)$$

$$= 550 \frac{\text{ft}}{\text{sec}} \left(\frac{1{,}000}{2.20} \text{ g}_f\right), \tag{4-3}$$

and so forth.

4-3 The Formulation of a Numerical Equation for Inconsistent Units

For the sake of repetitive calculations, it is often advantageous to convert an equation into a numerical form that will accommodate particular units. If one keeps in sight the idea that a physical variable is mathematically invariant, such transformations are simple. How they may be accomplished may be shown by an example.

The physical relationship between volume flow rate, area normal to flow path, and mean flow velocity may be written physically as

$$Q = AV. \tag{4-4}$$

If one is not working with consistent units, a good deal of conversion may be involved to get the desired results from this equation. As an example, if one is supplied with area in square inches and velocity in feet per minute and desires flow in gallons per hour, normal procedure would involve a change in units for both the area and velocity going into the equation and the flow coming out of it. If such conversions must be made repeatedly, the timesaving approach is clearly to rewrite the equation as a numerical equation appropriate for the desired units.

The safest way to accomplish this transformation is to define new variables, Q', A', and V', as the numbers associated with the desired units. These variables are then related to the physical variables Q, A, and V by the equations

$$Q = Q' \text{ gal/hr}, \tag{4-5}$$
$$A = A' \text{ in.}^2, \tag{4-6}$$
$$V = V' \text{ ft/min}. \tag{4-7}$$

If we substitute these variables into Eq. (4-4), we get

$$Q' \text{ gal/hr} = A' \text{ in.}^2 \, V' \text{ ft/min}, \tag{4-8}$$

or

$$Q' = A'V' \frac{\text{in.}^2\text{ft-hr}}{\text{gal-min}}. \tag{4-9}$$

The equation now contains the desired variables but also has tacked to it an undesired collection of units. This may easily be removed, however, by converting the units present to consistent units:

$$Q' = A'V' \frac{\text{in.}^2\text{ft-hr}}{\text{gal-min}} \left(\frac{\text{ft}^2}{144 \text{ in.}^2}\right) \left(\frac{3{,}600 \text{ sec}}{\text{hr}}\right) \left(\frac{7.48 \text{ gal}}{\text{ft}^3}\right)$$
$$\left(\frac{\text{min}}{60 \text{ sec}}\right)$$

$$= \frac{3{,}600 \cdot 7.48}{144 \cdot 60} A'V' = 3.12 \ A'V'. \tag{4-10}$$

The transformation could have proceeded along several slightly different lines. One technique that is less obvious, but possibly neater, is to rewrite the original equation so that the terms represent the numerical factors associated with consistent units and then convert these factors. For example, Eq. (4-4) may equally be written

$$\left(\frac{Q}{\text{ft}^3/\text{sec}}\right) = \left(\frac{A}{\text{ft}^2}\right)\left(\frac{V}{\text{ft}/\text{sec}}\right). \tag{4-11}$$

We may then convert these units to get what we want:

$$\left(\frac{Q}{\text{ft}^3/\text{sec}}\right)\left(\frac{\text{hr}}{3{,}600 \text{ sec}}\right)\left(\frac{\text{ft}^3}{7.48 \text{ gal}}\right)$$
$$= \left[\left(\frac{A}{\text{ft}^2}\right)\left(\frac{\text{ft}^2}{144 \text{ in.}^2}\right)\right]\left[\left(\frac{V}{\text{ft}/\text{sec}}\right)\left(\frac{\text{min}}{60 \text{ sec}}\right)\right] \tag{4-12}$$

This reduces to

$$\left(\frac{Q}{\text{gal}/\text{hr}}\right) = 3.12 \left(\frac{A}{\text{in.}^2}\right)\left(\frac{V}{\text{ft}/\text{min}}\right) \tag{4-13}$$

or

$$Q' = 3.12 \ A'V'. \tag{4-14}$$

If the original equation is itself a numerical equation, the technique is only slightly modified. If, for example, we wished to change the flow unit of Eq. (4-14) to gal/min, we could simply write

$$Q = Q' \text{ gal/hr} = Q'' \text{ gal/min}, \qquad (4\text{-}15)$$

whence

$$Q' = Q'' \frac{\text{hr}}{\text{min}} \left(\frac{60 \text{ min}}{\text{hr}} \right) = 60 \ Q''. \qquad (4\text{-}16)$$

Therefore

$$Q'' = \frac{3.12}{60} A'V' = 0.0520 \ A'V'. \qquad (4\text{-}17)$$

Alternatively we could rewrite Eq. (4-14) as Eq. (4-13) and convert the left-hand term to Q over gal/min.

Unless one proceeds in a mathematically logical manner, one may easily go awry in converting equations. The deceptive feature of such conversions is the inconspicuous fact that we are really aiming at a conversion of the numbers that multiply the units. Since these numbers change inversely as we change units, an intuitive approach to the problem is very likely to get the conversions backward.

4-4 The Formulation of a Physical Equation for Inconsistent Units

The end product of converting an equation so that it is appropriate for use with inconsistent units need not be a numerical equation. It is quite possible to write the result as a physical equation. Equation (4-13) is such an equation. We might rewrite this as

$$Q = 3.12 \ AV \frac{\text{gal-min}}{\text{in.}^2\text{ft-hr}} \qquad (4\text{-}18)$$

and have an equation which will automatically yield Q in gal/hr if A in in.^{2} and V in ft/min are substituted. Since having units cluttering up the equation is clearly unhandy, we may rewrite the equation as

$$Q = bAV, \qquad (4\text{-}19)$$

where

$$b = 3.12 \frac{\text{gal-min}}{\text{in.}^2\text{ft-hr}}. \qquad (4\text{-}20)$$

For some applications this scheme of writing equations for inconsistent units has advantages over using numerical equations. The factor b can be recognized as simply a conversion factor and is not restricted to only the value indicated by Eq. (4-20). Depending on what units one wishes to use in Eq. (4-19), it may take on a variety of values—including unity. The various equations we have written can be formed by appropriate selection from the following values of b:

$$b = 3.12 \frac{\text{gal-min}}{\text{in.}^2\text{ft-hr}} = 0.0520 \frac{\text{gal}}{\text{in.}^2\text{ft}} = 1. \qquad (4\text{-}21)$$

Besides its flexibility the physical equation with conversion factors present as symbols has the advantage over the numerical equation that the units of the magnitudes determined by the equation can be directly checked. For those who wish to deal generally with inconsistent units, therefore, it is usually safer to use this scheme. Many textbook writers have adopted this procedure for the sake of retaining some of the advantages of physical equations while avoiding the use of certain of the units that physical equations would normally require.

4-5 The Conversion of Concept

Instead of getting rid of unwanted units by introducing conversion factors into physical equations, one may sometimes accomplish this feat by converting the concept that has the undesirable unit to another that doesn't. This procedure introduces an extraneous factor into the equation, but not a factor that may properly be regarded as a unit-conversion factor.

A familiar example of such a factor is the acceleration of gravity. In many physical equations one finds this factor present for the sake of converting mass into weight. Although the conversion accomplishes a change in unit, the factor may not be regarded as a mere conversion factor; it is identifiable as a substantial physical variable always requiring units and never able to take on a value of unity.

The possibility of using concept-changing factors of this sort in much the same way that conversion factors are used is a source of a certain amount of confusion, particularly since the different factors may have the same numerical value. To convert mass in slugs to mass in pounds, we multiply by 32.174 lb_m/slug; to convert mass in slugs to weight in pounds, we multiply by 32.174 ft/sec² (if gravity is standard). Although one conversion changes only the unit, while the other changes the concept as well, they both involve the same number.

Problems and Examples

4-1. Using the equivalents listed below, make the following conversions:

    a. One centipoise to lb_m/hr-ft (viscosity).

    b. One kilowatthour to Btu (energy).

    c. One maxwell to webers (magnetic flux).

$$\text{dyne} = g_m\text{cm/sec}^2,$$
$$\text{newton} = kg_m\text{m/sec}^2,$$
$$\text{erg} = \text{dyne-cm},$$
$$\text{joule} = \text{newton-m},$$
$$\text{watt} = \text{joule/sec},$$
$$\text{maxwell} = \text{abvolt-sec},$$

$$m = 10^2 \text{ cm},$$
$$\text{poise} = 10^2 \text{ centi-}$$
$$\text{poises},$$
$$kw = 10^3 \text{ watts},$$
$$hr = 3{,}600 \text{ sec},$$
$$ft = 12 \text{ in.},$$

weber = volt-sec,   abcoulomb = 10
volt = joule/coulomb,   coulombs,
abvolt = erg/abcoulomb,   Btu = 778 ft-lb$_f$,
poise = dyne-sec/cm^2,   lb = 453.6 g,
kg = 10^3 g,   in. = 2.54 cm.

4-2. Certain experiments indicate that pressure loss through a needle valve may be described approximately by the equation

$$\Delta p = 0.09 \frac{\rho V^2}{D^{\frac{1}{3}}},$$

where Δp = pressure drop, lb/ft^2,
  ρ = density, slugs/ft^3,
  V = velocity at small end, ft/sec,
  D = diameter at small end, ft.

  a. Rewrite the equation as a physical equation.
  b. Determine the value of the factor in the equation if Δp is expressed in lb/in.^{2}, ρ in terms of the standard density of water (that is, as specific gravity), V in ft/sec, and D in inches.
  c. Is the factor a conversion factor?
  Solution. *a.* The equation may be rewritten as

$$\left(\frac{\Delta p}{\text{lb/ft}^2}\right) = 0.09 \left(\frac{\rho}{\text{slugs/ft}^3}\right) \left(\frac{V}{\text{ft/sec}}\right)^2 \left(\frac{\text{ft}}{D}\right)^{\frac{1}{3}},$$

in which the symbols now stand for the physical variables. This may be rewritten as

$$\Delta p = \frac{b\rho V^2}{D^{\frac{1}{3}}},$$

where $b = 0.09 \left(\frac{\text{lb}_f}{\text{ft}^2}\right) \left(\frac{\text{ft}^3}{\text{slugs}}\right) \left(\frac{\text{sec}}{\text{ft}}\right)^2 (\text{ft})^{\frac{1}{3}}$

  $= 0.09 \text{ lb}_f\text{sec}^2/\text{slug-ft}^{\frac{2}{3}}$
  $= 0.09 \text{ ft}^{\frac{1}{3}}.$

b. The transformation is most easily accomplished by altering the units of b as first stated:

$$b = 0.09 \left(\frac{\text{lb}_f}{\text{ft}^2}\right)\left(\frac{\text{ft}^2}{144 \text{ in.}^2}\right)\left(\frac{\text{ft}^3}{\text{slugs}}\right)\left(\frac{1.94 \text{ slugs}}{\text{ft}^3 \, \rho_o}\right)\left(\frac{\text{sec}}{\text{ft}}\right)^2$$

$$(\text{ft})^{1/3} \left(\frac{12 \text{ in.}}{\text{ft}}\right)^{1/3}$$

$$= \frac{0.09 \, (1.94) \, (12)^{1/3}}{144} \left(\frac{\text{lb}_f}{\text{in.}^2}\right)\left(\frac{1}{\rho_o}\right)\left(\frac{\text{sec}}{\text{ft}}\right)^2 (\text{in.})^{1/3}$$

$$= 0.0028 \text{ lb}_f \text{sec}^2/\rho_o \text{ ft}^2\text{in.}^{5/3}$$

(The unit $\rho_o = 1.94$ slugs/ft^3 is the standard density of water.)

c. The factor has the dimension of length to the one-third and cannot therefore be simply a conversion factor. (What variables are concealed in this factor are hard to imagine. The only possibility would appear to be some unnamed length. Because of the dimensional character of b, one must be suspicious of the generality of the correlation.)

4-3. The Napier rule for critical flow of steam through a nozzle is

$$m = \frac{pA}{70},$$

where m = flow, lb$_m$/sec,
   p = absolute pressure, lb$_f$/in.^{2},
   A = nozzle area, in.^{2}

a. Rewrite the equation as a physical equation appropriate for the units indicated.

b. Rewrite the equation as a physical equation appropriate for mass flow in lb$_m$/hr, pressure in lb/in.^{2} gage, and nozzle diameter in in.

4-4. The physical equation relating power to torque and speed is

$$P = T\omega,$$

where P = power transmitted by shaft,

$\quad$ T = torque transmitted by shaft,

$\quad$ ω = angular speed of shaft.

$\quad$ a. What are the consistent units for this equation corresponding to fundamental units of lb_f, ft, and sec?

$\quad$ b. Rewrite the equation as a numerical equation appropriate for hp, lb_fft, and rpm.

$\quad$ c. Rewrite the equation as a physical equation appropriate for the units of part b.

4-5. The physical equation for the ideal velocity from a nozzle is

$$V = \sqrt{2(h_o - h)},$$

where V = exit velocity,

$\quad$ h_o = reservoir enthalpy per unit mass,

$\quad$ h = exit enthalpy per unit mass.

$\quad$ a. Rewrite the equation as a numerical equation that will yield V in ft/sec from h in Btu/lb_m.

$\quad$ b. Rewrite the equation as a physical equation that will yield V in ft/sec from h in Btu/lb_m, making use of the conversion factors $g_c = 32.174$ lb_mft/lb_fsec^2 and $J = 778$ ft-lb_f/Btu.

5

The Units and
Dimensions of Mechanics

5-1 Introduction

In this chapter and the two that follow, many of the systems of units that have developed will be examined. A system of units, in the present context, is a selected array of units adequate for the description of the physical concepts one is concerned with. The formation of a system involves simply the selection of a single unit for each concept. For most systems the units are consistent; however, consistency is not an essential requirement. In the present sense, the metric and British systems of units are not true systems, since they provide a variety of units for each concept.

If everyone agreed on a standard meaning for each physical variable, if everyone agreed to describe physical behavior directly in terms of these variables, if everyone agreed to leave conversion factors out of such descriptions, and if everyone agreed to adopt the same fundamental units, then there would be only one sys-

60

tem of units. But agreement exists on none of these points. There is a tendency toward agreement on the first, but even there the agreement is still imperfect.

Our main interest in the various systems is to find a reasonable basis for agreement on this first point—to discover or establish a consistent meaning for the various physical variables described by the various systems. To arrive at this consistent meaning, one is forced to adopt essentially arbitrary interpretations of certain systems—interpretations discordant, but not incompatible, with the philosophies on which these systems were presumably based.

At the end of each chapter the dimensional pictures suggested by the various systems of units are considered and the standard dimensional system indicated. As previously explained, the standard system is essentially the system that reflects the conventional view of how units are related mathematically. The standard system usually reflects also the way in which units are established physically; however, the physical tie is usually established for the sake of the mathematics.

The first systems of units for mechanical concepts followed the scheme of regarding the units of mass, length, and time as fundamental and derived all other units from these. The three systems considered first in what follows are of this type. Later, the idea of considering force rather than mass to be fundamental was introduced. Only one system of this sort is in common use, but several other systems can be interpreted as derivatives of it.

5-2 The Defining Equations of Mechanics

The most important law relating the units of mechanics is Newton's law that force F is proportional to mass m times acceleration a. The accepted standard form of the law is simply

$$F = ma. \tag{5-1}$$

Although it is now a well-established custom to regard this equation as fundamental, it is not the only alternative. If the idea of kinetic energy rather than inertia were used to define mass, the relationship between force and mass would probably be different. Starting with the concept of energy, one would logically equate energy to mass times velocity squared, without inserting the extraneous factor of ½; force would then turn out to be twice the mass times the acceleration. Fortunately, no common systems use this starting point, and one possible source of confusion is eliminated. All systems are compatible with Eq. (5-1) as the relationship between force and mass—or at least may be made compatible by proper interpretation.

Most other fundamental concepts in mechanics are also defined by laws or rules that may be written the same for all systems (barring conversion factors). Viscosity, for example, is defined by an equation of the form

$$\tau = \mu \frac{dV}{dy}, \tag{5-2}$$

where τ = shear stress,
  μ = viscosity,
  V = velocity,
  y = distance.

Therefore viscosity has the dimensions of FT/L^2 in any system, with units to match (presumably).

Although it is necessary to name only the three basic units of a system, most systems name both the force and mass units (if both concepts are present). The derived units (unless they are accorded separate names of their own) are then usually expressed in terms of either the force or the mass unit, depending on the basis for their definition. Viscosity is a notable exception to this rule. The units of viscosity, though logically in terms of force, length, and time, are often expressed in terms of mass, length, and time. The apparent reason for this practice is that viscosity is often associated with density, and the association is simpler if the two concepts are expressed both in mass units or both in force units. Since the mass dimensions of viscosity are M/LT—simpler and hardly less comprehensible than the force dimensions FT/L^2—the practice of expressing viscosity in mass units is not surprising. Although it might in some ways be more satisfactory to express density in force units (particularly because of its role in describing inertia force and kinetic energy), the force dimensions of density are the complex and obscure array FT^2/L^4, which are hard to accept in place of the simple and easily comprehended M/L^3. Because of their unique treatment, the alternative units of viscosity are indicated in several of the systems described.

5-3   The Foot-Pound-Second System

The foot-pound-second system uses familiar British units for mass, length, and time: the foot for length, the pound for mass, and the second for time. The unit of force, the poundal, is defined as the force needed to accelerate one pound at the rate of one foot per second per second. From Newton's law, therefore, the poundal may be related to the pound, foot, and second by the equation

$$\text{poundal} = \frac{\text{lb}_m\text{ft}}{\text{sec}^2}. \qquad (5\text{-}3)$$

Other mechanical units derive from the accepted definitions of mechanics. Viscosity, for example, being the ratio of stress to a velocity gradient [Eq. (5-2)], has units of

$$\frac{\text{poundals/ft}^2}{(\text{ft/sec})/\text{ft}} = \frac{\text{poundal-sec}}{\text{ft}^2} \, . \tag{5-4}$$

Equation (5-3) permits alternative units for viscosity by substitution of the $\text{lb}_m\text{ft/sec}^2$ for the poundal:

$$\left(\frac{\text{lb}_m\text{ft}}{\text{sec}^2}\right)\frac{\text{sec}}{\text{ft}^2} = \frac{\text{lb}_m}{\text{sec-ft}} \, . \tag{5-5}$$

The units of Eqs. (5-4) and (5-5) are identical in meaning. The ft-lb-sec system (at least in its pure form) is little used.

5-4   The Centimeter-Gram-Second System

The centimeter-gram-second (cgs) system is developed in the same manner as the ft-lb-sec system but uses units from the metric system: the centimeter for length, the gram for mass, and the second for time. The unit of force, the dyne, is defined in the same manner as the poundal of the ft-lb-sec system and is therefore related to the basic units of the system by the equation

$$\text{dyne} = \frac{\text{g}_m\text{cm}}{\text{sec}^2} \, . \tag{5-6}$$

As is prevalent in systems using metric units, certain other derived units are also named. The unit of viscosity is the poise:

$$\text{poise} = \frac{\text{dyne-sec}}{\text{cm}^2} = \frac{\text{g}_m}{\text{cm-sec}} \, ; \tag{5-7}$$

the unit of kinematic viscosity (viscosity over density) is the stoke:

$$\text{stoke} = \frac{\text{cm}}{\text{sec}^2} \; ; \qquad\qquad (5\text{-}8)$$

and the unit of energy is the erg:

$$\text{erg} = \text{dyne-cm.} \qquad\qquad (5\text{-}9)$$

5-5 The Meter-Kilogram-Second System

The meter-kilogram-second (mks) system can be regarded as a practical modification of the cgs system, the only difference being that it uses larger units for length and mass. The force unit is aptly called the newton and has the equivalent units

$$\text{newton} = \frac{\text{kg}_m\text{m}}{\text{sec}^2} \cdot \qquad\qquad (5\text{-}10)$$

Since the kilogram is 10^3 g and the meter is 10^2 cm, the newton is 10^5 dynes.

The energy unit of the mks system, the newton-meter, is also called the joule; it has a magnitude of 10^7 ergs in terms of the cgs unit. The power unit is the watt, which is 1 joule/sec.

5-6 Treatment of the Force Unit

The force unit that arises in these three systems tends to be treated as a stepchild. The layman's unit of force is tied to the unit of mass through the action of gravity rather than the action of a unit acceleration. The force-pound, defined as the force exerted on a mass-pound by standard gravity (32.174 ft/sec^2) and therefore equal to 32.174 poundals, is preferred by the layman over the poundal. The force-gram and force-kilogram are similarly preferred over the dyne or newton (1 g_f = 980.7 dynes; 1 kg_f = 9.807 newtons). The engineer (being part layman) commonly practices duplicity—as may the scientist. When he talks of force, he will use pounds, grams, or kilograms, but when he substitutes force into an equation, he will use poundals, dynes, or newtons (assuming that he embraces one of the foregoing systems).

5-7 The Foot-Slug-Second System

The foot-slug-second system gets around the problem of the force unit by using the pound for this purpose, shifting the unwelcome burden of a new unit onto mass. The unit of mass is called the slug and is defined as the mass that will accelerate at the rate of one foot per second per second under the action of a force of one pound. The slug therefore is equivalent to 32.174 lb_m and is related to the basic units of the system by the equation

$$\text{slug} = \frac{lb_f\text{sec}}{ft^2} \cdot \qquad (5\text{-}11)$$

The slug has gained much more popularity as a mass unit than the poundal has as a force unit. One even occasionally finds data expressed in slugs. The chance of its taking over the job of the mass-pound completely, however, is remote.

Force-centered systems making use of metric units could easily be formed but are not in general use, at least in the pure form.

5-8 The Gravitational Foot-Slug-Second System

If the rule of labeling a system by its length, mass, and time units were adhered to, the gravitational ft-slug-sec system would merit the label of the ft-blank-sec system. Although using the pound as a unit of force, it manages to avoid using the slug by avoiding the use of mass; instead of talking about mass one talks about weight. Weight, being defined as the force exerted by gravity, is legitimately expressed in pounds in the ft-slug-sec system. If the mass of an object ever needs to be dealt with, it is expressed as the weight divided by the acceleration of gravity. Newton's law, for example, is written

$$F = \frac{W}{g} a, \qquad (5\text{-}12)$$

in which W is weight (in pounds).

The gravitational system is not so much a new system of units as a new system of variables. In the gravitational system, data that are properly referred to mass are instead referred to weight. A specific volume (volume per unit mass) of 10 ft^3/lb_m, for example, would be expressed as a specific volume (volume per unit weight) of 10 ft^3/lb_f, provided of course that the gravitational field were standard. (On the moon it would have to become something like 50 ft^3/lb_f.) Density is similarly treated, though it usually rates special treatment besides: users of the gravitational system relabel it specific weight and normally give it a new symbol. Water having a density of ρ = 62.4 lb_m/ft^3, for example, would have a specific weight (earthbound) of w = 62.4 lb_f/ft^3. The treatment accorded density should properly be accorded the other variables whose reference is changed, since they are really different concepts; but this propriety is normally ignored.

This way of treating mass—or rather of avoiding treating it—is popular among textbook writers and doubtless among students as well. As long as one keeps one's feet on the ground, or nearly so, the approach is all but foolproof. The distinction between force and mass is never a problem, because mass is not in the picture. One might, however, question the desirability, from a pedagogical point of view, of shielding the student from the concept of mass, a concept that too long ago found its way into the literature of science to be easily ignored.

Another objection that might be raised against the system is that it tends to obscure the influence of gravity. Equations that have nothing at all to do with gravity are still likely to have the acceleration of gravity present in their terms. As a simple example, the speed of sound in a homogeneous medium would be written

$$a = \sqrt{\gamma \, gpv}, \tag{5-13}$$

where γ = isentropic exponent,
 g = acceleration of gravity,
 p = absolute pressure,
 v = specific volume.

The only reason for the g is that the specific volume v is referred to weight rather than mass. If g changes, v does as well, leaving the influence of gravity nil.

The space-minded members of the aeronautical profession have quite naturally developed an aversion to this scheme and generally have decided to acknowledge mass as a useful concept even if it means accepting the slug. In the pure ft-slug-sec system, with v defined in the natural way, Eq. (5-13) reads

$$a = \sqrt{\gamma p v}, \tag{5-14}$$

with a in ft/sec, p in lb/ft^2, and v in ft^3/slug. For a civilization stumbling over the threshold of the Space Age it would seem a more sensible form.

5-9 The Two-pound System

The two-pound system is an effort to enjoy most of the benefits of the gravitational system without suffering the consequences of dealing with physical variables inappropriate for the physical situation. The pound is used for both mass and force: essentially what is done is to put a conversion factor into Newton's law (and all relations deriving from it) which converts the pounds substituted for mass into slugs. Newton's law is written

$$F = m \frac{a}{g_c}, \tag{5-15}$$

where g_c is the dimensionless conversion factor,

$$g_c = 32.174 \frac{\text{lb}_m \text{ft}}{\text{lb}_f \text{sec}^2} = 32.174 \frac{\text{lb}_m}{\text{slug}}. \tag{5-16}$$

With this factor present, a substitution of m in lb_m and acceleration in ft/sec^2 gives force in lb_f.

If one feels compelled to tamper with the mass unit, this is probably the most defensible way to go about it. About all that one may be justifiably accused of is solving a simple problem in a difficult way. Rather than accepting the chore of remembering that mass must be converted to slugs, one prefers to take on the chore of remembering the location of dozens of g_c's which serve only to make this conversion.

In the two-pound system a conversion factor is normally introduced into the shear law also. With the usual shear law, the units of viscosity for the two-pound system are $\text{lb}_f \text{sec}/\text{ft}^2$. But most users of the system are not happy with such units—apparently because they necessitate a conversion factor in Reynolds number—and alter the system so that $\text{lb}_m/\text{sec-ft}$ may serve for viscosity. This requires slipping g_c into the shear law.

A somewhat different interpretation is sometimes given to the system. Some advocates prefer to regard the factor g_c as a physical constant having the dimensions ML/FT^2, rather than a mere conversion factor. The primary effect of such a move is that it rescinds the mathematical relationship between force and mass units. Although there is no inherent harm in doing this, the fact of life exists that most other systems admit a relationship. For the sake of a consistent structure of units one must reasonably yield to the will of the majority.

One might take the advocates of such a "four-dimensional" system more seriously if they didn't admit alien "three-dimensional" ideas to their system. With four distinct dimensions the option of expressing a concept in mass or force units at will doesn't exist. No reasonable stretch of the imagination could justify any units but $lb_f sec/ft^2$ for viscosity, for example. Users of the system, however, normally covet the units lb_m/sec-ft for viscosity and get them into the system by the most transparent of artifices: in effect, they denote viscosity as normally defined by the symbol μ_f, define a new variable $\mu_m = \mu_f g_c$, and then transfer the name of viscosity to the new variable. This move is clearly illogical in the context of the system; it would be equally justifiable—and equally illogical—to divide μ_f by the universal constant of gravitation G to give μ_m units of $lb_m{}^2 sec/ft^4$. The latter move would make sense if the law of gravitation were accepted as establishing a relationship between force and mass units; and the former move makes sense only if the law of motion is accepted in this role. If it is accepted, the four dimensions of the system are not independent.

5-10 The Problem of the Pound

The various schemes that have been put forward to make the pound usable for describing both mass and force concepts have been responsible for much confusion. The distinction between mass and weight seems to be the major problem. Weight is so often used in situations where mass is proper that it is easy to forget that it is a distinct, if related, concept.

One source of confusion is the failure to recognize that the relationship between the units of mass and weight is not a relationship between the concepts of mass and weight. The units are related by the equation

$$\text{lb}_f = 32.174 \ \text{lb}_m \text{ft/sec}^2. \qquad (5\text{-}17)$$

This equation in itself, however, tells nothing about how the mass and weight of a particular object are related. It only says that a weight of one pound has a weight of 32.174 $\text{lb}_m \text{ft/sec}^2$ (which is a weight of 32.174 poundals); it clearly does not say that a weight of one pound has a mass of 32.174 lb_m. If gravity is standard, a weight of one pound will have a mass of one pound, as may easily be deduced from Newton's law [along with Eq. (5-17)]:

$$m = \frac{W}{g} = \frac{1 \ \text{lb}_f}{32.174 \ \text{ft/sec}^2} = 1 \ \text{lb}_m. \qquad (5\text{-}18)$$

In other words, converting from mass to weight is not the same as converting from mass units to weight (or force) units. A conversion from mass to weight is not merely a conversion of units: it is also a change of concept. If, for example, a gas has a specific volume of 10 ft^3/lb_m when referred to its mass, it will have a specific volume of 10 ft^3/lb_f when referred to its weight (gravity being standard). The two specific volumes are, however, different variables having different dimensions and obeying different rules of behavior. By contrast, a viscosity of 10 $\text{lb}_f\text{sec}/\text{ft}^2$ becomes 322 $\text{lb}_m/\text{sec-ft}$ if the force units are changed to mass units. Here only the units of measurement are changed by a dimensionless conversion; the concept is identical.

5-11   The Dimensions of Mechanics

From the way in which the units have developed it is evident that the dimensions of mass, length, and time or force, length, and time are normally regarded as fundamental in mechanics. There is, of course, the dissident minority who would prefer to regard force, mass, length, and time, all as fundamental; but, as indicated, this viewpoint clashes with what must be regarded as the conventional viewpoint of the structure of units. As we shall see in a later chapter, this minority viewpoint is valid; we reject it only because it is incompatible with the majority opinion of how units are related.

If dynamic effects occupy a subordinate position, one may sometimes see other dimensions regarded as fundamental; in electrical studies, for example, one might find force described as having dimensions of current squared times resistance times length over time. One might reasonably be suspicious of a dimensional system that needs four dimensions to describe a mechanical concept when three should suffice; however, such a system is not inevitably wrong. Regarding current, resistance, length, and time as fundamental turns out to give effectively only three dimensions to mechanical concepts: energy (in the form of current squared times resistance), length, and time.

Problems and Examples

5-1. Is it possible to construct a system of units in which the lb_f and lb_m are consistent units of force and mass, without upsetting the conventional relationships among units? What would be the units of absolute and kinematic viscosity in such a system?

Solution. If mass is defined as the force per g of acceleration—that is, if g_o is used as a unit of acceleration—the lb_f and the lb_m will be consistent units. If the second is retained as a unit of time, then the unit of length would have to be 32.174 ft (or g_o sec^2).

The unit of viscosity would be lb_fsec/(32.174 ft)^2 or lb_f/g_o^2 sec^3, which would have the equivalent of lb_m/g_o sec^3 or $lb_m/(32.174$ ft) sec. The unit of kinematic viscosity would be the unit of viscosity over $lb_m/(32.174$ ft)^3 or lb_m/g_o^3 sec^6 (the unit of density), which would be (32.174 ft)^2/sec or g_o^2 sec^3.

5-2. If a system of units were based on Newton's law in the form

$$F = m \frac{a}{g_o},$$

where $g_o = 32.174$ ft/sec^2, then the lb_m and the lb_f could be consistent units of mass and force.

 a. What would be the consistent units of length and time?

 b. How would the relationship between the lb_m and the lb_f compare with the system of Prob. 5-1?

 c. What would be the units of viscosity in terms of force and mass units, and how would they be related to the units of the ft-slug-sec system?

 d. What would be the units of kinematic viscosity, and how would they be related to units of the ft-slug-sec system?

 5-3. If a system of units employed the United States gallon for volume, the mile per hour for velocity, and the horsepower for power, what would be the consistent units of length, time, force, and mass and how would they be related to the ft, sec, lb_f, and lb_m, respectively?

5-4. If the volume, velocity, and power units of Prob. 5-3 were used in conjunction with the mile for length, the hour for time, the lb_f for force, and the lb_m for mass, what conversion factors would appear in the physical forms of Newton's law, the equation for volume of a cube, and the equation for power in terms of force and velocity?

5-5. In terms of the gram as a unit of mass, the dyne as a unit of force, the centimeter as a unit of length, and the second as a unit of time, Newton's law of motion and gravitation and the equation for the speed of light in free space take the form

$$F = ma,$$

$$F = G\frac{m_1 m_2}{r^2},$$

where $G = 6.67 \cdot 10^{-8}$ dyne-cm^2/g$_m{}^2$; and

$$c = 3 \cdot 10^{10} \text{ cm/sec.}$$

For a system of units in which G and c are assigned values of unity, demonstrate the following:

a. The units of force, mass, length, and time are defined in terms of a single artificial standard.

b. The unit of force is independent of that standard and equal to $1.21 \cdot 10^{49}$ dynes.

5-6. Commonly encountered units in nuclear physics are the "atomic mass unit" ($1.6604 \cdot 10^{-24}$ g) for mass, the electron volt ($1.602 \cdot 10^{-12}$ erg) for energy, and the barn (10^{-24} cm^2) for area. If these units are used as a basis for forming a consistent system of units, what would be the units for force, length, and time, and what would be their magnitude in terms of cgs units?

6

The Units and Dimensions of Thermodynamics and Heat Transfer

6-1 Introduction

To define the concepts of thermodynamics, a new fundamental unit—a unit of temperature—is normally introduced. A complete set of units can be formed by adding an arbitrarily defined unit of temperature to the list of mechanical units of force (or mass), length, and time and proceeding to define the derived units of thermodynamics directly from the basic equations in their simplest form. Such an approach is simple and logical.

But the demands of custom have somewhat disrupted the smooth processes of logic. Thermal units developed before the relationship between thermal and dynamic effects was appreciated. In deference to the thermal units, thermodynamic systems of units are likely to be of a hybrid character that requires the presence of conversion factors in the basic equations. The burden of conversion factors need not be borne, however, and some writers choose to cast it off.

The principal equation relating the units of thermodynamics is the first law, which relates heat to work. The second law serves the important function of defining temperature, as well as relating entropy, heat, and temperature. The units of other thermodynamic variables are generally obtainable from their defining equations.

The parameters of heat transfer require no additional fundamental units beyond what is provided by thermodynamics.

6-2 Temperature

The idea that temperature is a measure of molecular activity might lead one to imagine that temperature might appropriately be defined in terms of energy. The relationship of temperature to energy is not a general one, however, and though it might serve to define the unit of temperature, it is unsatisfactory for defining the concept. It would be mathematically permissible to identify the unit of temperature with a unit of energy (see Prob. 6-4); however, there is commonly a reluctance to erect a conventional tie between units unless it has very nearly universal significance. Since the concept of temperature exists independent of any molecular notion of matter, it has generally been deemed more appropriate to regard its unit as well as its conception independent of molecular description.

The proper definition of a temperature unit has not been easy. Unlike mass, length, and time, temperature is not an extensive concept: that is, larger amounts cannot simply be formed by reduplication of smaller amounts. Early efforts to define temperature related it to expansion characteristics of particular materials. In most respects such a definition is satisfactory; however, one senses that a proper definition of temperature should involve an arbitrary specification of only the size of the fundamental unit, not of the whole scale of units.

The problem of the temperature scale was solved (at least conceptually) by the second law. The law revealed how a selected temperature unit could be reduplicated without reference to the properties of a particular substance, thereby giving temperature the fundamental definition it presumably deserved.

The temperature unit used by systems deriving from the metric system is the degree Celsius or centigrade (the former term now being preferred) and by systems deriving from the British the degree Fahrenheit. The present basis for the size of the Celsius unit is the specification that there are 273.16°C between absolute zero and the triple point of water. The Fahrenheit degree is defined as being smaller by the factor 1.8. The Celsius unit is used in the Celsius and the Kelvin temperature scales, the two scales differing only in location of the zero (at the ice point on the Celsius scale and at absolute zero on the Kelvin). The Fahrenheit unit is used in the Fahrenheit and the Rankine scales, which are also simply related (the zeros being 32° below the ice point and at absolute zero, respectively). By the usual convention temperatures on the absolute scales are labeled degrees Kelvin (°K) or degrees Rankine (°R). As far as the units themselves are concerned, however, °K = °C and °R = °F.

The temperature labels are examples of labels that serve partly as unit labels and partly as concept labels. From the standpoint of units it would be less confusing to label absolute temperature with the same unit as ordinary temperature: for example, one might better say that the absolute temperature is 520°F (properly distinguishing the temperature by an adjective) than say that temperature is 520°R (dropping the adjective from temperature and improperly distinguishing the unit). Nearly the same effect is obtained by saying that the temperature is 520°F abs; even though the adjective is strangely positioned, the usage conforms with other conventional usage (for example, lb/in.² abs for absolute pressure) and is less likely to be misleading. Although some writers use the °F abs and °C abs notation, the °R and °K notation is generally more popular; the fact that it may be less logical is not likely to promote its discard.

The imperfect notation of temperature has led to certain mathematically illegal practices that have been mentioned in a previous chapter. It is quite common to say that 60°F = 520°R, and it is seemingly correct logic: if (1) the temperature is 60°F and (2) the temperature is 520°R, then (3) 60°F = 520°R. But the equation is not valid mathematically (certainly °F/°R $\neq$ 8.67) and arises only from faulty notation. If one properly says that the Fahrenheit temperature is 60°F and the Rankine (or absolute) temperature is 520°R (or °F), the equality wouldn't follow. The two temperatures are really different concepts; equating them is much like saying that 1 lb$_m$ = 1 lb$_f$. As with so many of the illegal practices of science and engineering, however, it is more important to recognize the illegality than to avoid the practice.

Some writers seek to minimize the confusion over the meaning of the temperature unit by using different symbols to denote the unit and the scale. The letter alone is used to denote the unit, the degree sign being reserved for denoting temperatures on the scale. By this notation one would say that 60F—without the degree sign—is equivalent to 60R (since presumably

temperature differences are referred to), but 60°F—
with the degree sign—is equivalent to 520°R (since
here the temperature level is referred to). The scheme
can hardly be praised for solving the basic problem,
but at least it makes it more evident that a problem
exists; and certainly it reminds one that the conversion
of units (C, F, K, R) follows different rules from the
conversion of concepts (°C, °F, °K, °R). But in the
final analysis one may reasonably argue that, as long
as the notation is wrong, why not keep it simple?

6-3 The Units of Heat

The first law of thermodynamics defines heat in
terms of work and provides a mechanical basis for defining the units of heat. One statement of the law says
that the net amount of heat added during a cyclic
process must equal the net work done:

$$\oint dQ = \oint dW. \qquad (6\text{-}1)$$

If this simple form of equation is selected, the units of
heat are identical to the units of work: ft-lb$_f$ in the ft-
slug-sec system, ergs in the cgs system, and so on.

The accepted units for heat in the British and metric
systems, however, were originally defined without relation to work, being based instead on the calorimetric
properties or water. If these units, the Btu and calorie,
are to be used, Eq. (6-1) has to be rewritten

$$J \oint dQ = \oint dW, \qquad (6\text{-}2)$$

where the conversion factor J (Joule's constant) takes
on a value such as 778 ft-lb/Btu or 4.186 joules/cal, depending on the system of units used.

The quantity J was originally a conversion factor of

uncertain value. Since work and heat units were independently defined, the numerical value of J was dependent on a measured property of water. With the heat unit tied to the specific heat of water at a specified temperature, J was effectively a measure of the "specific work" of water (ft-lb$_f$/lb$_m$°F in British units) at the specified temperature. It is now generally agreed, however, to detach the heat units from their calorimetric definitions and relate them directly to mechanical (or electrical) energy units. According to the IT (International Steam Table) definitions one calorie equals $^{180}/_{43}$ joules exactly (or one watt-hour equals 860 calories). With this change J earns the permanence befitting a dimensionless conversion factor between units.

Many textbooks retain J in the thermodynamic equations; but with its recognition as a mere conversion factor its presence is not essential. If J is absent, heat, work, and other forms of energy are simply expressed in the same unit. The arguments for including J are similar to the arguments for including g_c, and so are the countering arguments.

6-4 The Units of Heat Transfer

The conventional units of heat transfer, as used in America, do not fit into any of the systems normally used in thermodynamics or mechanics. The major distinction is the use of the hour as the unit of time, presumably because heat flow ordinarily takes rather a long time to add up to much. Heat is expressed in Btu, mass in pounds. Length is normally measured in feet; however, some writers prefer to measure distance along a path of heat conduction in inches, a practice that gives rise to the interesting units of Btu per hr-ft^2-(°F/in.) for conductivity. Although such conductivity units are sometimes used for data, they are not normally incorporated into a system of units.

6-5 The Dimensions of Thermodynamics and Heat Transfer

One usually encounters the conventional dimensions of thermodynamics expressed in terms of the dimensions of mechanics plus the temperature dimension (θ). Heat and work, thermal and mechanical energy, therefore have dimensions of FL or ML^2/T^2; specific heat and entropy have dimensions of $FL/M\theta$, which reduces to $L^2/T^2\theta$.

One sometimes finds heat regarded as a fifth dimension. Such a viewpoint would probably deserve prevalence if the conversion factor between work and heat were an experimental parameter, as it once was. But since its value has been fixed by decree, the more prevalent and more logical notion is that heat has the dimensions of force times length; and the accepted relationships among units follow this rule.

Problems and Examples

6-1. Write the equation relating temperature in °C to temperature in °F as a physical equation.

6-2. What are the dimensions of specific heat (heat transfer per unit of mass per unit of temperature rise), heat-transfer coefficient (heat transfer per unit of area per unit of temperature difference), and thermal conductivity (heat transfer per unit of area per unit of temperature gradient), in terms of M, L, T, and θ?

6-3. The following equations are examples of how the energy equation for a steady-flow system is written in various textbooks. The first equation is the standard physical equation and may be interpreted as describing the energies (transported or transferred) per slug of flow. Determine the units (as conventionally described) appropriate for each variable of these equations. Relate each variable of the last three equations to the corresponding physical variables of the first equation:

$$u_1 + p_1v_1 + \frac{1}{2}\,V_1{}^2 + gz_1 + Q$$

$$= u_2 + p_2v_2 + \frac{1}{2}\,V_2{}^2 + gz_2 + W,$$

$$u_1 + \frac{p_1v_1}{Jg_c} + \frac{V_1{}^2}{2Jg_c} + \frac{g}{g_c}\frac{z_1}{J} + Q$$

$$= u_2 + \frac{p_2v_2}{Jg_c} + \frac{V_2{}^2}{2Jg_c} + \frac{g}{g_c}\frac{z_2}{J} + W,$$

$$u_1 + \frac{p_1v_1}{J} + \frac{V_1{}^2}{2Jg} + \frac{z_1}{J} + Q$$

$$= u_2 + \frac{p_2v_2}{J} + \frac{V_2{}^2}{2Jg} + \frac{z_2}{J} + W,$$

$$u_1 + \frac{144p_1v_1}{778} + \left(\frac{V_1}{223.8}\right)^2 + \frac{gz_1}{(32.2)(778)} + Q$$

$$= u_2 + \frac{144p_2v_2}{778} + \left(\frac{V_2}{223.8}\right)^2 + \frac{gz_2}{(32.2)(778)} + W,$$

where u = internal energy,
p = absolute pressure,
v = specific volume,
V = velocity, ft/sec,
g = acceleration of gravity, ft/sec^2,
Q = heat added,
W = work done,
J = 778 ft-lb$_f$/Btu,
g_c = 32.174 lb$_m$ft/lb$_f$sec^2.

6-4. The temperature unit could be defined by assigning a definite magnitude to Boltzmann's constant

k, the gas constant of a molecule ($k = 1.3802 \cdot 10^{-16}$ erg/°K). Such a course would invite considering k a dimensionless conversion factor—that is, identifying the dimensions of energy and temperature.

a. Show that such a viewpoint would make the entropy of a system dimensionless. Is such a conclusion ever reasonable?

b. Under what circumstances might the dimensional picture resulting from considering k dimensionless be permissible?

Solution. a. Since entropy can be evaluated as a ratio of heat transfer (that is, energy) to temperature, it has the same dimensions as k and will become dimensionless if k is made dimensionless. In some systems entropy can be directly related to the probability of the state of the system and therefore is an effectively natural variable. This possibility is not generally regarded as universal, however, and therefore the naturalness of entropy is dependent on the system considered.

b. If a system is analyzed in terms of molecular behavior, this dimensional picture is likely to be permissible. Where a system is analyzed in terms of macroscopic properties, however, the constancy of k is not normally pertinent and therefore the identification of the dimensions of temperature and energy would be inappropriate.

7

The Units and
Dimensions of Electricity

7-1   Introduction

The units of electricity have had such a complicated
history that it is not a simple matter to arrive at a consistent interpretation of them.   In mechanics or thermodynamics all the common schemes for defining units are
compatible with a consistent physical interpretation of
the equations in which they are involved.   In electricity,
however, certain of the still popular systems of electrical units are associated with equations that may not
properly be given a physical interpretation.

Where there are competing philosophies—such as are
exemplified by the competing systems of electrical
units—there is always the question of which philosophy
shall be used as the basis for defining consistent units.
We answer this question in a way that seems easily defended; however, the answer is essentially arbitrary,
and in the end its validity depends on accepted practice.
Since many users of electrical units refrain from giving
them a full mathematical meaning, it is not always
obvious what constitutes accepted practice.   An appar-

84

ent agreement has been reached, however, on how various units of the same sort are related mathematically; and implicit in this agreement is an acceptance of certain forms of the equations of electricity as the standard physical equations. Although these physical equations of electricity may not always appear clearly identified, it seems safe to say that they are nevertheless now clearly established.

To be consistent with this viewpoint, some of the equations that define the cgs units considered first in what follows cannot be given a physical interpretation. In particular, some of the relationships between units that follow logically from the ideas in the next three sections have to be abandoned if subsequent developments in concept are acknowledged.

In discussing cgs units we shall follow the practice of labeling certain of the units by the "practical" name preceded by the prefix stat- or ab- depending on whether the unit derives from a law between charges or a law between poles. As an example, we shall denote the electrostatic cgs unit of voltage as the statvolt and the electromagnetic unit as the abvolt.

7-2   Gaussian Units

Gaussian units may be interpreted as deriving from the cgs units of mechanics, Coulomb's law of force between electrical charges in free space, and an analogous (artificial) law between magnetic poles. The two laws may be written

$$F = \frac{q_1 q_2}{\epsilon_o r^2} \tag{7-1}$$

and

$$F = \frac{p_1 p_2}{\mu_o r^2}, \tag{7-2}$$

where F = force, dynes,

$\quad\quad r$ = distance between charges or poles, cm,

$\quad\quad q$ = charge strength,

$\quad\quad p$ = pole strength,

$\quad\quad \epsilon_o$ = permittivity of free space,

$\quad\quad \mu_o$ = permeability of free space.

The unit of charge (called the statcoulomb) and the unit of pole strength (called the pole—or sometimes the abpole, to make its origin clearer) are defined by specifying that ϵ_o and μ_o have a value of unity. Therefore two unit charges or two unit poles a centimeter apart in a vacuum exert a force on one another of one dyne. For the formulation of Gaussian units, the presence of ϵ_o and μ_o in Eqs. (7-1) and (7-2) is somewhat artificial; however, subsequent developments in units suggest a reinterpretation of Gaussian units that would make this presence of ϵ_o and μ_o essential. For the sake of things to come, therefore, we include these factors, even though for the moment they should logically be absent.

The popular tendency today is to avoid at all costs using a law between magnetic poles in the definition of electrical units. Since the concept of a magnetic pole as an entity analogous to an electric charge has been completely discredited, the argument against its use is obvious. On the other hand, any attempt to avoid its use runs into artificialities that are not essentially different, but only better concealed. Whether one chooses to define magnetic field strength as an inherently artificial concept or to define it as a natural concept growing out of the definition of the artificial concept of a magnetic pole would seem to make little essential difference. The magnetic pole is a satisfactory mathematical concept that is given precise meaning by virtue of the relationship between electrical and magnetic effects. In the final analysis, the fact that it has no physical analogue should not discredit its use in establishing the mathematical structure of units. Since it makes the framework of electrical units simpler, we consequently use it.

The concepts of field strength and electromotive or magnetomotive force are defined in an obvious manner. Electric field strength E is the force exerted on a unit charge (dynes/statcoulomb); magnetic field strength H is the force exerted on a unit pole (dynes/pole). The latter unit is also called the oersted. Electromotive force (emf) V_e is the work done in moving a unit charge (ergs/statcoulomb, called statvolts); magnetomotive force (mmf) V_m is the work done in moving a unit pole (ergs/pole, called gilberts). Electric potential and magnetic potential have the same units as emf and mmf, respectively.

Flux concepts may also be defined. Electric flux ϕ_e and magnetic flux ϕ_m are given units called lines (or sometimes statlines) and maxwells, respectively. The size of the flux units is determined by defining electric flux density D as ϵE and magnetic flux density B as μH; the unit of B (maxwells/cm²) is called the gauss. The full meaning of flux, and of permittivity ϵ and permeability μ, is established by specifying a one-to-one correspondence between electric flux and charge and magnetic flux and pole strength. From the force laws and the definition of flux, it may be determined that 4π units of flux are associated with a unit charge or pole:

$$\phi_e = 4\pi q, \qquad (7\text{-}3)$$
$$\phi_m = 4\pi p \ (= 0). \qquad (7\text{-}4)$$

[If these equations are rigorously interpreted as giving the flux through a closed surface, the parenthetic equality of Eq. (7-4) must hold in any physical situation, because of the acknowledged impossibility of enclosing a net pole strength within such a surface.] The same result may be expressed in a different form, using vector notation, as

$$\operatorname{div} D = 4\pi\rho, \tag{7-5}$$
$$\operatorname{div} B = 0, \tag{7-6}$$

where ρ is charge density. The divergence (div) is a space derivative.

The list of basic concepts may be completed by defining a current unit in the natural manner, that is, as a statcoulomb per second. This unit (the statampere) is the only logical choice if one accepts Coulomb's laws as the basis for the Gaussian system and is the one we shall adhere to; however, many users of Gaussian units prefer the abampere of the emu system (Sec. 7-3) as the unit of current.

The picture of Gaussian units is not really complete unless the equations that relate electric and magnetic phenomena are inspected. Faraday's law of voltage induction and the Ampère-Maxwell law of mmf take the following form (integrated and differential):

$$V_e = -\frac{1}{c'}\frac{d\phi_m}{dt} \qquad \text{or} \quad \operatorname{curl} E = -\frac{1}{c'}\frac{\partial B}{\partial t}, \tag{7-7}$$

$$V_m = \frac{1}{c'}\left(4\pi I + \frac{d\phi_e}{dt}\right) \text{ or } \operatorname{curl} H = \frac{1}{c'}\left(4\pi J + \frac{\partial D}{\partial t}\right), \tag{7-8}$$

where V_e, V_m = emf and mmf round a closed loop,
ϕ_e, ϕ_m = electric and magnetic flux linked by loop,
I = linked current,
J = current density.

The right-hand equations are vector equations in which the curl is a space derivative. These equations, which are the basic equations relating electric and magnetic variables, introduce a new parameter c' into the picture. An interpretation of c' may be secured by looking at the vector form of these equations.

In a charge-free field in which ϵ and μ are constant, Eqs. (7-7) and (7-8) may be rewritten

$$\text{curl } E = -\frac{1}{c'} \mu \frac{\partial H}{\partial t}, \tag{7-9}$$

$$\text{curl } H = \frac{1}{c'} \epsilon \frac{\partial E}{\partial t}. \tag{7-10}$$

If these are combined to eliminate H, one gets [using the fact from Eq. (7-5) that the divergence of E is zero in a charge-free field]

$$\Delta E = \frac{1}{c'^2} \mu\epsilon \frac{\partial E}{\partial t}, \tag{7-11}$$

where Δ is the Laplacian (a second space derivative). (Elimination of E would give the same equation in H.) This equation may be recognized as a wave equation in which the propagation velocity is 1 over the square root of the coefficient of the time derivative (that is, $c'/\sqrt{\mu\epsilon}$). Since μ and ϵ have values of unity for free space, c' may therefore be identified as the propagation velocity of electromagnetic waves in free space, or in popular terms the velocity of light. The new parameter is therefore not a variable but a universal constant having the approximate value $3 \cdot 10^{10}$ cm/sec (more accurately $2.9978 \cdot 10^{10}$). Its identification supplies a mathematical meaning to the concepts of pole strength, magnetic field strength, and permeability.

7-3 Electrostatic and Electromagnetic Units

Because of the relationship between electrical and magnetic variables provided by Faraday's law (or the Ampère-Maxwell law), several alternatives to the Gaussian system of units immediately suggest themselves. One may either start with the Gaussian electric units and define new magnetic units through Faraday's law or start with the Gaussian magnetic units and proceed in the opposite direction. Adopting either of these procedures, the logical form for Faraday's law would be the simplest, namely, without the constant factor c'. The two systems of units formed in this fashion are called electrostatic units (esu) if derivable from Coulomb's law for charges and electromagnetic units (emu) if derivable from Coulomb's law for poles. For either of these systems Eqs. (7-7) and (7-8) take the form

$$V_e = -\frac{d\phi_m}{dt} \qquad \text{or} \qquad \text{curl } E = -\frac{\partial B}{\partial t}, \quad (7\text{-}12)$$

$$V_m = 4\pi I + \frac{d\phi_e}{dt} \qquad \text{or} \qquad \text{curl } H = 4\pi J + \frac{\partial D}{\partial t}. \quad (7\text{-}13)$$

The use of esu for magnetic concepts is rare, but not the use of emu for electric concepts, particularly current. The definition of the emu of current is easy to reach. Equation (7-12) provides a magnetic definition of emf: a flux change of one maxwell per second will induce one emu of voltage (an abvolt). An emu of charge (the abcoulomb) may then be defined as a charge experiencing a force of one dyne in a field having a strength of one abvolt per centimeter. The abampere then follows as an abcoulomb per second. In emu the permittivity ϵ would not be unity for a vacuum, but takes on a value of $1/c'^2$ (as does μ if expressed in esu). The relationship between emu and esu is rather a strange one. An inspection of the equations reveals that

$$1 \text{ statvolt} = c' \text{ abvolts}, \qquad (7\text{-}14)$$
$$1 \text{ abampere} = c' \text{ statamperes}. \qquad (7\text{-}15)$$

The factor between the two units is not a true conversion factor but has the dimensions of velocity and units of cm/sec. One is led to the conclusion that esu voltage and emu voltage, esu current and emu current, etc., are really different concepts; in fact, it appears that a change from esu to emu amounts to a change in all concepts, and not just a change in units.

7-4   Reinterpretation of the Dimensional Constant

The idea that corresponding esu and emu concepts are different is a rather disagreeable one. However, it may be demonstrated that merely by a reinterpretation of the meaning of c' the incompatibility of esu and emu concepts may be eliminated, though at the expense of giving D, E, B, and H all different dimensions.

To make esu and emu compatible, it is evident that c' must be regarded as a dimensionless conversion factor rather than a dimensional constant. This specification may be met if ϵ and μ are permitted to have dimensions in the Gaussian system. If this notion is accepted, it may not be said that ϵ for free space is unity, but rather that it has a value of one line/statvolt-cm; similarly μ for free space would be one maxwell/gilbert-cm (or one gauss/oersted). With this change in viewpoint, Eq.

(7-11) would indicate a free-space velocity of light, not of c', but rather of

$$c = \frac{c'}{\sqrt{\mu_o \epsilon_o}}, \qquad (7\text{-}16)$$

where μ_o and ϵ_o would have unity magnitude but units as indicated above. Substitution of the units will give (with some manipulation)

$$c' = c\sqrt{\mu_o \epsilon_o} = 3 \cdot 10^{10} \frac{\text{maxwells}}{\text{statvolt-sec}}. \qquad (7\text{-}17)$$

A change from Gaussian units to emu or esu may then be interpreted as a change from inconsistent units, for which c' has the value in Eq. (7-17), to consistent units, for which $c' = 1$. In emu, for example, the statvolt of Gaussian units is replaced by the abvolt, of such size that c' becomes

$$c' = \frac{\text{maxwells}}{\text{abvolt-sec}} = 1. \qquad (7\text{-}18)$$

A comparison of Eqs. (7-17) and (7-18) then indicates that

$$1 \text{ statvolt} = 3 \cdot 10^{10} \text{ abvolts}. \qquad (7\text{-}19)$$

The conversion between the esu and the emu of voltage may therefore be interpreted as merely a change in size of unit. Other conversions may be shown to have the same character.

With this interpretation of c' there would appear to be no obstacle to regarding the various equations we have written as physical equations. Certain other features of the equations, however, have apparently also interfered with the natural tendency to give equations a physical interpretation. In particular the relationship between flux and charge seems to suggest that these variables should not be assigned the same unit, as a physical interpretation would demand. Since 1 unit of charge gives rise to 4π units of flux, it seems physically more reasonable to regard the unit of charge as being 4π times as large as the unit of flux. This presumption makes it impossible to interpret the equations as physical equations. It also gives rise to the idea of rationalization.

7-5 Rationalized Units

By a few changes it is possible to remove the factor 4π that relates flux to charge or pole strength. This removal of the 4π factor is called rationalization. A possible approach to rationalization would be to introduce appropriate changes of variable. One might, for example, introduce a new flux variable ϕ'_e which is $1/4\pi$ times the old flux variable. Then the unrationalized equation for flux from a charge q,

$$\phi_e = 4\pi q, \tag{7-20}$$

would become

$$\phi'_e = q. \tag{7-21}$$

A simple change of this sort would permit both the rationalized and the unrationalized equations to be interpreted as physical equations; however, it would have awkward consequences. If accepted as physical equations, these equations would indicate that a flux of 1 statcoulomb in the rationalized system would correspond to a flux of 4π statcoulombs in the unrationalized system. The difference would arise not from a redefinition of the statcoulomb but from a redefinition of the meaning of flux. Though such a redefinition is permissible, it would undoubtedly be the source of much confusion.

A better approach is to consider the flux the same, but its units different in each system. For this to be true, only one of the equations can be regarded a physical equation. The logical choice is to regard the rationalized equation as a physical equation, thereby giving rationalized flux and charge corresponding units as well as corresponding magnitudes. We therefore accept as the proper physical relationship between ϕ_e and q:

$$\phi_e = q. \tag{7-22}$$

With this selection, the unrationalized units of flux and charge must be accepted as different and the unrationalized equation relating flux and charge as a numerical equation. We have already denoted the unrationalized units of flux and charge by the terms lines and statcoulombs, respectively. To be expressed as a physical equation, therefore, Eq. (7-20) must be written

$$\phi_e = 4\pi q \text{ lines/statcoulomb}, \tag{7-23}$$

which yields the proper unrationalized result that 1 statcoulomb of charge yields 4π lines of flux.

The unrationalized physical equation is obtainable from the rationalized expression by the mere insertion of a conversion factor:

$$\phi_e = b_q q. \tag{7-24}$$

The conversion factor b_q has the value of

$$b_q = \frac{4\pi \text{ lines}}{\text{statcoulomb}} \tag{7-25}$$

in the unrationalized system and unity in the rationalized system.

This line of interpretation permits rationalization to be regarded as a mere removal of conversion factors by selection of consistent units. In unrationalized units the unit of charge is 4π times as big as the unit of flux, where in rationalized units both concepts are expressed in an identical unit. It should probably be borne in mind, however, that such a conclusion depends on accepting Eq. (7-22) as the defining equation for flux. With less reason, though perhaps greater historical justification, one might have accepted Eq. (7-20) as the defining equation for flux and identified the line with the statcoulomb.

Similar arguments can be directed to the magnetic side of the picture. In rationalized units the magnetic flux is related to pole strength as

$$\phi_m = p. \tag{7-26}$$

The unrationalized expression is then

$$\phi_m = b_p p, \tag{7-27}$$

where

$$b_p = 4\pi \text{ maxwells/pole.} \tag{7-28}$$

Several alternative choices of units are clearly possible for the rationalized flux equations. Electric flux and charge can both be expressed in statcoulombs or both in lines; magnetic flux and pole strength can both be expressed in maxwells or both in poles. Although the choice is arbitrary, the combination of lines and poles, or statcoulombs and maxwells, is preferable to the other two possibilities because it preserves the identity of the factor c' in the Gaussian equations. This fact can be seen easily from Eq. (7-7): if the units of V_e or E, which are related to the statcoulomb, and the units of ϕ_m or B, which are related to the maxwell, are either both changed or both left unchanged, the factor c' will not have to be altered.

The choice that has been made in rationalization is to retain the Gaussian units of charge and magnetic flux (the statcoulomb and the maxwell) and to drop the line and the pole. This alters the unit of magnetic field strength and mmf but leaves electric field strength and emf unchanged. The unit of current is also unchanged. To render the various equations complete, the following replacements are necessary:

$$D \rightarrow D \text{ statcoulombs/line} = \frac{4\pi}{b_q} D \qquad (7\text{-}29)$$

(and similarly for ϕ_e),

$$H \rightarrow H \text{ poles/maxwell} = \frac{4\pi}{b_p} H \qquad (7\text{-}30)$$

(and similarly for V_m),

$$p \rightarrow p \text{ maxwells/pole} = \frac{b_p}{4\pi} p, \qquad (7\text{-}31)$$

$$\epsilon \rightarrow \epsilon \text{ statcoulombs/line} = \frac{4\pi}{b_q} \epsilon, \qquad (7\text{-}32)$$

$$\mu \rightarrow \mu \text{ maxwells/pole} = \frac{b_p}{4\pi} \mu. \qquad (7\text{-}33)$$

These are changes of the same sort as made in changing the numerical equation (7-20) to the physical versions (7-23) and (7-24).

With these replacements the Gaussian equations take the form

$$\phi_e = b_q q \qquad \text{or} \quad \text{div } D = b_q \rho, \qquad (7\text{-}34)$$
$$\phi_m = b_p p (= 0) \quad \text{or} \quad \text{div } B = 0, \qquad (7\text{-}35)$$
$$V_e = -\frac{1}{c'}\frac{d\phi_m}{dt} \quad \text{or} \quad \text{curl } E = -\frac{1}{c'}\frac{\partial B}{\partial t}, \quad (7\text{-}36)$$

or
$$\frac{1}{b_p} V_m = \frac{1}{c'}\left(I + \frac{1}{b_q}\frac{d\phi_e}{dt}\right)$$
$$\frac{1}{b_p}\text{ curl } H = \frac{1}{c'}\left(J + \frac{1}{b_q}\frac{\partial D}{\partial t}\right), \qquad (7\text{-}37)$$

$$D = \epsilon E, \qquad (7\text{-}38)$$
$$B = \mu H, \qquad (7\text{-}39)$$

$$F_q = b_q \frac{q_1 q_2}{4\pi\epsilon_o r^2}, \qquad (7\text{-}40)$$

$$F_p = b_p \frac{p_1 p_2}{4\pi \mu_o r^2} . \tag{7-41}$$

The unrationalized Gaussian equations can be obtained from these by replacing b_p and b_q by 4π. The equations so obtained are essentially numerical equations, since the units don't check, but if the units associated with 4π were substituted, they would be complete physical equations. The rationalized equations are obtained by replacing b_p and b_q by unity.

The rationalized units are all related to the ordinary Gaussian units by a factor of 4π or else are unchanged. In rationalized units electric flux is expressed in statcoulombs rather than lines, the rationalized unit being larger by a factor of 4π. Magnetic pole strength is expressed in maxwells rather than poles, the rationalized unit being smaller by the same factor. The unit of magnetic field strength, dynes/maxwell, is accordingly $1/4\pi$ times as large as the unrationalized unit of dynes/pole. Magnetic potential, or mmf, is similarly expressed in a unit $1/4\pi$ times as large (ergs/maxwell rather than ergs/pole); the new unit, incidentally, can be identified with the abampere.

In the rationalized system the units of both ϵ and μ are changed. The unit of ϵ becomes larger: statcoulombs/statvolt-cm rather than lines/statvolt-cm. The unit of μ becomes smaller: it may be identified in emu as maxwells/abamp-cm rather than poles/abamp-cm. For free space, therefore, ϵ has the magnitude $1/4\pi$ and μ the magnitude 4π.

Choosing to regard the rationalized equations as physical equations and the unrationalized equations as numerical equations is clearly arbitrary. It is probable, however, that the majority of users of the unrationalized equations have always regarded them as numerical equations and have not considered them to provide relationships among the various units. As previously suggested, the ordinary user probably chooses not to identify the esu of charge and flux or the emu of pole strength and flux. Whatever the truth may be, however, it is now generally agreed that the esu of flux is $1/4\pi$ times as big as the statcoulomb of flux and that the emu of pole strength is 4π times as big as the maxwell of pole strength. Whether fully deserved or not, history has reduced the unrationalized equations to the status of numerical equations.

Although users of Gaussian units seem willing to accept the rationalized equations as providing the proper defining equations for flux units, they seem less willing to use the equations themselves. The chief use of rationalization is in conjunction with practical units.

7-6   Practical Units

Electrical data are usually expressed in what are called practical units. These units are an odd mixture of cgs and mks units. Magnetic variables are expressed in emu: maxwells, gauss, gilberts, oersteds, etc. The current unit, the ampere, is taken as one-tenth of an abampere; the corresponding charge of an ampere-second is called the coulomb. The unit of electric potential, the volt, is defined using the energy unit (the joule) from the mks system: a volt has a value of 1 joule/coulomb, and volts times amperes yields joules/second, or watts, the mks power unit. Electric field strength, however, would probably be expressed "practically" as volts/centimeter, which has the interesting equivalent of newton-meters/coulomb-centimeter.

By inclusion of a sufficient number of conversion factors in the equations, a system using only practical units is of course possible. Such a system, however, is not in common use.

7-7 The Meter-Kilogram-Second System

A consistent system based on the practical units of current and voltage is the latest development in electrical units. Since the ampere and volt are consistent with the mks system of mechanics, that system is used for mass, force, length, and time units. To develop the remaining units, all conversion factors (including c') are set equal to unity. The resulting system is usually called merely the mks system, though it is sometimes more rigorously called the practical rationalized mks system (or the Giorgi system) to distinguish it from other systems based on the meter, kilogram, and second but still involving conversion factors (implicitly).

With all conversion factors (b_p, b_q, and c') removed, Eqs. (7-34) through (7-41) become

$$\phi_e = q \qquad \text{or} \qquad \text{div } D = \rho, \tag{7-42}$$

$$\phi_m = p \; (= 0) \qquad \text{or} \qquad \text{div } B = 0, \tag{7-43}$$

$$V_e = - \frac{d\phi_m}{dt} \qquad \text{or} \qquad \text{curl } E = - \frac{\partial B}{\partial t}, \tag{7-44}$$

$$V_m = I + \frac{d\phi_e}{dt} \qquad \text{or} \qquad \text{curl } H = J + \frac{\partial D}{\partial t}, \tag{7-45}$$

$$D = \epsilon E, \tag{7-46}$$

$$B = \mu H, \tag{7-47}$$

$$F_q = \frac{q_1 q_2}{4\pi \epsilon_o r^2}, \tag{7-48}$$

$$F_p = \frac{p_1 p_2}{4\pi \mu_o r^2}. \tag{7-49}$$

(The same equations would hold for rationalized esu or emu.)

Starting with the meter, kilogram, second, and a single electrical unit, one can define all other units from these equations plus Newton's law in the form $F = ma$. If the coulomb is selected as the electrical unit, the ampere, or coulomb/second, follows as the unit of current and the volt, or joule/coulomb, as the unit of electric potential or emf. Electric field strength is then expressible as volts/meter or newtons/coulomb. Electric flux (like charge) has units of coulombs. With these units, the permittivity turns out to have units of coulombs/volt-meter or farads/meter and has a magnitude of approximately $(36\pi \cdot 10^9)^{-1}$ for free space.

The magnetic units are defined through Eqs. (7-44) and (7-45). The first of these equations leads to the conclusion that the unit of magnetic flux is the volt-second; for denoting flux (or pole strength), the volt-second is commonly referred to as the weber. The second of these equations reveals that the unit of mmf (or magnetic potential) is the ampere; when used to denote mmf, the ampere is sometimes called the ampere-turn. The remaining magnetic units are easily derived. Field strength comes out as either newtons/weber or amperes/meter. The permeability is then webers/ampere-meter or henrys/meter and has a magnitude of $4\pi \cdot 10^{-7}$ for free space. (In establishing the physical standards for electrical units the latter magnitude is taken as exact by definition, whereas the permittivity of free space is regarded as an experimental constant.)

Because of the absence of extraneous factors in the relationships between the various electrical variables, the mks equations have probably quite naturally been given a physical interpretation that was ordinarily denied the Gaussian or the unrationalized esu or emu equations. The fact that they are interpreted as physical equations is probably the chief reason that they have gained most favor with the engineer, who normally has a greater stake in keeping units straight.

7-8 The Dimensions of Electricity

From the foregoing it is probably evident that there is room for several points of view on the dimensions of electrical and magnetic concepts. Not only the kind of dimensions but the number as well may be disputed. The effect of the alternative dimensional pictures on the formulation of physical description will be considered in the next chapter. For the present we shall consider only the more obvious aspects of form.

If one accepts the original philosophy on which Gaussian units were based, one finds that only three dimensions are needed to describe all concepts; and those three may be taken as the same that are used to describe the dimensions of mechanics. If ϵ and μ are considered dimensionless, Coulomb's laws indicate that charge and pole strength have dimensions of $F^{1/2}L$, from which it follows that D, E, B, and H all have dimensions of $F^{1/2}/L$. Voltage and mmf get dimensions of $F^{1/2}$ and current $F^{1/2}L/T$ (giving voltage times current the proper power dimensions of FL/T). With just force, length, and time (or mass, length, and time) as fundamental dimensions, all the dimensions of electricity may be deduced.

Systems of dimensions may also be based on the ideas implicit in the esu and emu systems of units. In esu the electric concepts would have Gaussian dimensions, but magnetic concepts would rate different dimensions: Faraday's law would give magnetic flux the dimension of $F^{1/2}T$ rather than the Gaussian $F^{1/2}L$; permeability would show dimensions of T^2/L^2 rather than none. The emu dimensions would take analogous form, with ϵ

gaining dimensions of T^2/L^2. A rational justification for either of these systems of dimensions is difficult. If one permits μ to have dimensions (as in the esu system), one may not very convincingly argue that ϵ should be denied them, and vice versa.

The alternative interpretation of the equations of electricity—that ϵ and μ are properly considered dimensional factors and that c' is properly regarded as a dimensionless factor rather than the speed of light— gives rise to a system involving four fundamental dimensions. Such a system may be established with the least alteration of the previous concepts simply by regarding the dimension of either ϵ or μ to be fundamental. Voltage, for example, can be given the dimensions $F^{1/2}/\epsilon^{1/2}$ (in terms of F, L, T, and ϵ) or $F^{1/2}\mu^{1/2}L/T$ (in terms of F, L, T, and μ). These fundamental dimensions are simply related to esu or emu dimensions: the latter are obtainable by simply dropping out the ϵ or μ, respectively. Although these systems represent consistent alternatives to the Gaussian system, the choice of fundamental dimensions is awkward.

A more logical and fundamental choice of a fourth dimension would appear to be charge. With such a choice the system becomes more closely related to conventional units—particularly mks units. Using F, L, T, and Q, one may fairly quickly decide on the dimensions: current would be Q/T; electric field strength, F/Q; voltage, FL/Q. The magnetic side would be brought in through Faraday's law, which indicates that magnetic flux has dimensions of voltage times time, or FLT/Q. Since pole strength has the same dimensions as magnetic flux, magnetic field strength (force per unit pole) would have dimensions Q/LT. This would give mmf the dimensions Q/T, the same dimensions as current (as mks units would indicate).

An alternative approach would be to bring in a fifth dimension, P for pole strength, using it for expressing magnetic ideas, but remembering in the final analysis that $PQ = FLT$ (much as one commonly brings in both F and M in talking about mechanical concepts but sheds one in favor of the other in the end).

If four dimensions are regarded as fundamental, many other possibilities are available. One may choose to consider only two of the dimensions of mechanics fundamental and add two electrical dimensions to make out the list. This approach may have the disadvantage—as we've already seen in the selection of length, time, current, and resistance—of giving rise to rather complicated arrays for simple mechanical ideas; however, in many electrical situations it might prove the most effective approach. Very often, particularly in electricity, the best choice of dimensions is dependent on the problem at hand.

Since the equations exemplified by the rationalized mks system are now regarded as the standard physical equations relating electrical and magnetic variables, the four-dimensional systems formed by regarding μ and ϵ as dimensional variables and c' as dimensionless are properly regarded as defining the conventional dimensions of electricity. The Gaussian system of dimensions (which considers μ and ϵ dimensionless), the esu system (which considers ϵ dimensionless), and the emu system (which considers μ dimensionless) must therefore be viewed as unconventional or special systems that have no present-day counterpart in accepted relationships among units.

Problems and Examples

7-1. The magnetic flux density B may be defined either through the idea of voltage induction or through the idea of the force on a current-carrying wire. The first notion would lead to defining the unit of B as the flux density that would induce a unit of voltage in a suitably oriented circuit of unit area, if varied at the rate of one unit per unit time. The second notion would lead to defining the unit of B as the force per unit length of conductor per unit of current (on a suitably oriented wire). Show that either approach defines the same unit.

Solution. Since these definitions are compatible with the mks units, it is perhaps easiest to consider how they apply to those units. The first definition would identify the unit of B per second with the volt per square meter. The unit of B could therefore be expressed as volt-sec/m². Giving the name of weber to the volt-sec, one gets the conventional nomenclature weber/m².

The second definition would identify the unit of B with the newton/amp-m. Since 1 newton-m/sec (or watt) is equal to 1 volt-amp, this may be reexpressed as volt-sec/m² as before.

7-2. Determine how the following units are related to the ampere, ohm, meter, and second (the units indicated are consistent with these four):

   a. Farad (capacitance)

   b. Henry (inductance)

   c. Coulomb (electric flux)

   d. Weber (magnetic flux)

7-3. What is the relationship of the gilbert (the Gaussian unit of mmf) to the abampere? To the mks unit?

7-4. What is the permittivity of free space in abfarads/cm?

7-5. What are the dimensions of resistance R, capacitance C, and inductance L in terms of force, length, time, and charge? In terms of resistance, current, length, and time? Based on dimensions, which of the following choices is correct?

a. The time constant of an R-C circuit is equal to R/C, C/R, or RC.

b. The time constant of an R-L circuit is equal to R/L, L/R, or RL.

7-6. Show that, if permittivity, permeability, and the speed of light were all considered dimensionless and equal to unity for free space, resistance would also be dimensionless and have a unit with a magnitude of 120π ohms. Explain why the unit so defined is natural.

8

The Nature of
Physical Relations

8-1 Introduction

In the preceding chapters we have seen how the relationships among physical variables give rise to relationships among dimensions. We now shall look at the more intriguing question of how the relationships among dimensions give rise to relationships among physical variables.

For this process to be fully effective, the relationships that are admitted among dimensions must be established in a natural manner. Dimensional relationships that simply reflect the way we have chosen to relate units may not always be appropriate or pertinent to a specific physical situation. Artificialities that may not detract from the effectiveness of a unit in establishing the magnitude of a physical variable may still give quite misleading ideas about the function of that variable in describing physical behavior. To understand how the essential nature of units—as expressed by the relationships among dimensions—guides the formulation of physical relations, it is necessary to be fully aware of which aspects of the relationships among units arise naturally and which do not.

8-2 The Formulation of Fundamental Laws

As we have seen, the formulation of fundamental laws and definitions is somewhat subject to the whim of the formulator. To understand the structure of physical relations, it is necessary to recognize what aspects of form are fundamental. It is also important to know what whims may properly be given license.

In this connection it is revealing to look again at the technique of translating a physical notion into mathematics. Our previous concern was how to arrive at a formulation that is compatible with the conventional meaning of the physical variables involved. Our present concern is how to arrive at a formulation that is compatible with the intrinsic meaning of the physical variables involved. In other words, we are not so much concerned with the existence of conventions as with their right to existence.

The viscous-shear law provides a simple example of how a physical notion may be expressed mathematically. The law states that in a Newtonian fluid the rate of distortion of the fluid is proportional to the shear stress. Strictly speaking, a Newtonian fluid is a hypothetical substance; however, for practical purposes a large number of fluids may be regarded as Newtonian without much error. For a unidirectional flow the rate of distortion is equal to the transverse derivative of velocity; therefore for such a flow the law may be stated in a numerical form as

$$\tau' = \mu' \frac{dV'}{dy'}, \qquad (8\text{-}1)$$

where μ' is a factor of proportionality. The shear stress τ, the velocity V, and the transverse coordinate y may be related to the variables of the equation as follows:

$$\tau = \tau' \text{ lb}_f/\text{ft}^2, \tag{8-2}$$
$$V = V' \text{ ft/sec}, \tag{8-3}$$
$$y = y' \text{ ft}. \tag{8-4}$$

If we combine these equations appropriately with Eq. (8-1), we may write

$$\frac{\tau}{dV/dy} = \mu' \text{ lb}_f\text{sec}/\text{ft}^2. \tag{8-5}$$

Since the left-hand side of the equation represents a physical variable, the right-hand side must as well. We therefore give it a name (viscosity) and a symbol:

$$\mu = \mu' \text{ lb}_f\text{sec}/\text{ft}^2. \tag{8-6}$$

With this identification we may write the law in the form of a physical equation:

$$\tau = \mu \frac{dV}{dy}. \tag{8-7}$$

To reach this point, we have presumed only what is implicit in Eqs. (8-2) to (8-4); namely, that the product of a number and a unit has a mathematical meaning. Beyond that we have assigned a symbol to the product of a particular number and unit and thereby defined a new physical variable. Experimentally we discover this new variable to be a property of the fluid.

There are clearly few options in the formulation of this law. The one thing we might have done is alter Eq. (8-6). The left-hand term could have been specified as $1/\mu$ or μ^2 or $4\pi\mu$, thereby changing the meaning of μ. But beyond this one instance, no occasion for arbitrary choice seems to be present.

In the formulation of certain other laws, somewhat

more freedom of choice is present. Newton's law of motion provides an example. The law may be stated by saying that force is proportional to mass times acceleration. To state it in this manner requires that we may define force and mass without reference to the law, but this is no real problem. Proceeding in the same manner as before, we could first write

$$F' = m' \frac{a'}{g'_c}, \qquad (8\text{-}8)$$

where g'_c is a proportionality factor whose magnitude would depend on the units used for force, mass, and acceleration. If the primed variables are related to the physical variables by the equations

$$F = F' \text{ lb}_f, \qquad (8\text{-}9)$$
$$m = m' \text{ lb}_m, \qquad (8\text{-}10)$$
$$a = a' \text{ ft/sec}^2, \qquad (8\text{-}11)$$

we could then write the relationship as the physical equation

$$F = m \frac{a}{g_c}, \qquad (8\text{-}12)$$

in which g_c is a newly defined physical variable having the value

$$g_c = g'_c \text{ lb}_m\text{ft/lb}_f\text{sec}^2. \qquad (8\text{-}13)$$

The result we have gotten by this procedure has one important difference from the previous result. Where μ was truly a variable, g_c is not. Since the law is not dependent on the medium, g_c is a universal physical constant.

The constancy of g_c permits us to go about setting up the law in a different manner. We might say instead that, for a given mass, force is proportional to acceleration, or

$$F' = m'a', \qquad (8\text{-}14)$$

where m' is now interpreted as the factor of proportionality. Repeating the previous steps, we would arrive at the physical equation

$$F = ma, \tag{8-15}$$

where m is defined as

$$m = m' \text{ lb}_f\text{sec}^2/\text{ft} \tag{8-16}$$

and of course is labeled the mass.

By common consent we regard Eq. (8-15) as the proper physical statement of Newton's law. We do not contend that the reasoning that leads to Eq. (8-12) is erroneous; we merely contend that the reasoning that leads to Eq. (8-15) is equally proper and yields a result that we prefer. Although we have tacitly defined mass (or force) through the equation instead of independently, it is still the same concept.

Characteristic of the three formulations that we have considered is the fact that we have done nothing that can be reasonably interpreted as artificial. In particular we have not assigned any arbitrary dimensions to the physical variable or constant arising from the law; we have let its definition arise in an entirely natural way.

8-3 The Nature of Physical Constants

Physical constants occur quite naturally in physical equations that relate previously identified concepts. Only if the equation serves to define a new physical variable is it likely to be written initially without recourse to a physical constant. If force, mass, and acceleration are regarded as concepts definable without reference to Newton's law, the logical statement of the law—at least at the outset—involves the physical constant g_c.

There is a tendency, however, for such physical constants to change character. This tendency may often be suppressed for practical reasons; but, in the instance of g_c, practical arguments favor the change. The first step in this change is to give the physical constant a precise magnitude. Initially g_c is experimental and therefore somewhat uncertain. Since g_c is theoretically a precise magnitude, it is conceptually comforting as well as mathematically desirable if this uncertainty is eliminated. This is easily accomplished if we use the notion implicit in Newton's law to define force in terms of mass (or vice versa). We have the alternatives of either defining a new unit of force or redefining the old unit. In practice we have usually done both, though normally the new unit is first created and the old unit redefined only after the new unit has gained acceptance as a standard. The normal transition for g_c would involve, for example, first defining the poundal as the unit of force that would give a unit acceleration to a pound of mass. This would fix the value of g_c at 1 lb-ft/poundal-sec^2. With the acceptance of the poundal so defined as a satisfactory unit of force, the force-pound would then be redefined in terms of the poundal—or in terms of mass and acceleration. For example, defining the force-pound as either 32.174 poundals or as the force that would accelerate a mass-pound at the rate of 32.174 ft/sec^2 would give g_c an immutable value in terms of the force-pound as well as the poundal. The practicality of making these moves depends on whether the new definition of force is as satisfactory as the old, for the uncertainty in the equation is shifted to the unit. In the instance of force the new definition is quite satisfactory.

Once a physical constant has been given a fixed value in this manner, the way is open for another change. By giving a physical constant a fixed value we endow it with the attributes of a dimensionless number. Once we have redefined the unit of force, no change in the size of the three physical standards on which the unit of g_c is based will change its numerical magnitude: any change in size of the mass-pound, the foot, or the second will be compensated by an appropriate change in the poundal or force-pound. Accordingly, g_c may legitimately be regarded as dimensionless if we so choose. Whether we so choose depends on whether we wish to admit the dimensional relationship that results into our conventional picture of dimensions. In the instance of g_c we have found it advantageous from most points of view to do so. Not the least of the arguments in favor of this move is the pervasiveness of g_c in the relations of science; by rendering it dimensionless we are able to assign it a value of unity and drop it from our equations.

This natural transition of a physical constant of uncertain magnitude to a dimensionless constant of precise magnitude—a mere conversion factor—is often halted somewhere along the line for practical reasons. Either the new definition of a unit may be inappropriate for general use, or the new dimensional picture may be unacceptable in the context of conventional experience.

The gravitational constant G is an example of a physical constant that hasn't followed the path of g_c to extinction—in spite of its theoretical and historical kinship. Newton's law of gravitation is normally written

$$F = G \frac{m_1 m_2}{r^2},   (8\text{-}17)$$

where G is interpreted as a physical constant having dimensions FL^2/M^2. It is possible to use this equation (in conjunction with Newton's law of motion) to relate the units of both force and mass to units of length and time. We may thereby give G a fixed value such as unity. If we carried this procedure to its natural conclusion, we should then regard G as dimensionless and identify M with L^3/T^2 and F with L^4/T^4. But we restrain ourselves from doing this for two good reasons. In the first place the law is very unhandy for defining a unit because of the puny force between measurable masses; for ordinary use we much prefer to stick with our artificial standard of mass. Furthermore, the dimensional picture arising from regarding G as dimensionless is foreign to conventional experience. Establishing a system of units that gives G a fixed value is certainly permissible and probably appropriate for special applications; however, we logically choose to regard the unit of mass of such a system as a unit having uncertain magnitude in conventional terms. Also, we conventionally regard G as possessing units even though its magnitude may be 1 in terms of appropriately defined units.

In some instances we may agree to give a physical constant a fixed magnitude but choose not to take the next step of regarding it as dimensionless. For example, we give to the permeability of free space a fixed value of $4\pi \cdot 10^{-7}$ henry/m; however—as discussed in the next section—we prefer not to consider permeability dimensionless because we don't like the dimensional picture that results.

Whether we reduce a physical constant to the status of a dimensionless conversion factor depends, therefore, partly on whether we can define an acceptable unit by such a move and partly on whether we are happy with the dimensional picture that such a move gives rise to. The choice—for whatever reason—is almost purely on practical grounds. No cosmic excuse can be given for choosing to regard g_c as dimensionless and G as not.

Fortunately this arbitrariness doesn't matter to the structure of physical description. When we accord the same treatment to a physical constant such as G that we do to a physical variable such as μ, we are suggesting that in some other world G might take on a different value. But just as treating μ as a physical variable does not hamper its application to situations where it is constant, so also treating G as if it were a physical variable does not distort the picture of a world in which it is not.

In spite of these arguments, however, one may occasionally perceive more clearly the nature of the physical world if one gives a conceptually proper interpretation to physical constants. Although there is no mathematical reason why constants such as g_c or G may not be treated as physical variables, the physical fact remains that they are not variables; and their lack of variability is a part of our concept of the universe. How a mathematical recognition of such constancy may be conceptually helpful may be seen from a consideration of the idea of relativity. The basic notion of relativity is that c, the speed of light in free space, is a universal constant. If we argue that c should therefore be regarded as dimensionless, we find that time earns the dimensions of length and mass of energy. While this dimensional identification hardly proves the convertibility of time and length, or of mass and energy, it at least sets the stage. As a somewhat more mundane example, the fact that we regard g_c as dimensionless gives kinematic viscosity ν the same dimensions as thermal diffusivity α and suggests their analogous roles in the diffusion of vorticity and heat.

But from the standpoint of mathematics these considerations are unimportant. Whether we say that α has the dimensions of ν or of νg_c makes little difference;

and whether we identify E with m or mc^2 is a small point.

8-4   Improper Formulation of Fundamental Laws

While we may apparently treat the physical constants that may arise in fundamental equations either as dimensional or dimensionless numbers as custom dictates, we cannot be allowed any more freedom with dimensions without upsetting certain properties of fundamental equations that we wish to preserve. We have already suggested that life among units would be much happier if we had chosen to write Newton's law as

$$F = m \frac{a}{g_o}, \qquad (8\text{-}18)$$

where g_o is the standard acceleration of gravity through which we relate the mass-pound and the force-pound. Such a specification, however, gives the proportionality factor in the equation arbitrary dimensions, as well as arbitrarily giving force the dimensions of mass.

The objectionable feature of such a move is that it defines a natural variable that is not essentially natural in the context of the law. With Eq. (8-18) accepted as the proper formulation of Newton's law, F/m becomes a natural variable; but there is no way in which the unit of F may be defined in terms of the unit of m without reference to some external standard. The variable F/m is therefore not properly regarded as dimensionless. The standard needed in this instance would of course be a standard gravitational field. In any situation where such a field is present and exerting influence, the formulation would be proper; however, Newton's law should clearly not be written in a way that restricts it to such applications—or at least makes it misleading when applied to other situations. Since we live constantly in a gravitation field, our natural conception of mass is in terms of gravitational force; but this is a special conception inappropriate for a general mathematical formulation of Newton's law.

Analogous arguments may be used in assessing the propriety of electrical formulations. The Gaussian concept that electrical flux density and electric field strength are dimensionally the same—in other words, that permittivity is dimensionless—is not without basis; however, from some points of view the basis is artificial. The Gaussian concept depends on free space—or at least a space free of polarization—as a reference. In a situation where no such space is involved, permittivity cannot be regarded as a natural variable, and its dimensionless form is inappropriate. The Gaussian formulation is therefore in some ways very similar to the formulation of Newton's law in the form of Eq. (8-18). It is based on a valid concept, but it happens that the concept is foreign to some applications of the equations and therefore is artificial from the standpoint of the equations themselves.

The formulation of the mks equations, on the other hand, involves no such artificiality. The equations may be set up without reference to free space. Free space enters the picture for the sake of establishing the size of the units, but it does not enter in the guise of a natural unit. The arbitrary choices made in the formulation of the mks system of equations do not distort or specialize the dimensions. It would be permissible to retain universal physical constants in the system (for example, in the equations that relate electric and magnetic concepts), but it is also permissible to regard these constants as dimensionless and equate them to unity.

Because of the intrinsic logic of its formulation, the dimensional picture exemplified by the mks system is usually regarded as the proper context for electrical description.

These conclusions depend, of course, on what we agree to regard as the basic notions of electricity. One may easily argue that a formulation involving permittivity and permeability ignores what is really going on and therefore does not deserve to be favored when we set about limning our conventional dimensional picture. One may easily contend that to ignore the pervasion of free space in any electrical problem is to ignore reality. But in our conventional macroscopic analysis of electrical behavior we commonly do not involve free space as an essential ingredient, and we therefore appropriately do not involve it in our conventional dimensional picture.

8-5 The Dimensional Nature of Fundamental Laws

One significant feature of fundamental laws and definitions is that they may always be written as physical equations. This statement may almost be considered a truism, but it is nevertheless important. As a consequence of this fact any fundamental law or definition may be described wholly in terms of natural variables: since the dimensions of all terms in a physical equation are inevitably the same, a ratio of any two terms is dimensionless and therefore a natural variable. Newton's law may be stated by saying that the natural variable F/ma is equal to unity—or if g_c were retained as a dimensional constant, Fg_c/ma would be equal to unity. Similarly the law of gravitation states that the natural variable Fr^2/Gm_1m_2 is unity; and Coulomb's law (as presently interpreted) assigns the value 4π to the natural variable $q_1 q_2 / F \epsilon r^2$. The existence of this general property of fundamental equations has an important bearing on the formulation of most physical relations.

8-6 The Form of Derived Relations

Any relation that is derived mathematically from fundamental laws or definitions must naturally fall heir to the essential dimensional consistency of the laws themselves. And, again, any such derived relation must also be susceptible to being written in terms of natural variables. For example, if the equation for the force on a sphere moving through a fluid could be derived by applying such fundamental notions as Newton's law and the shear law to the fluid, the result obtained would show the same dimensional consistency as the laws from which it derived and could therefore also be expressed as a relationship involving only natural variables.

As far as derived equations themselves are concerned, about the only practical significance of their dimensional consistency is in the check of completeness or correctness that it provides. If two terms of an equation have incompatible dimensions, one may conclude that something has been left out, or incorrectly included, or not properly identified. Dimensional consistency also requires that the arguments of trigonometric functions, exponential functions, and the like, should be dimensionless in physical relations. Perhaps the easiest way to see this necessity is to consider a power-series expansion of such a function, which will clearly be inconsistent dimensionally unless the argument is a dimensionless number. Of course, such maneuvers as splitting a logarithm into the sum of two logarithms may obscure the truth; but if appropriate consolidations are made, the rule will hold.

Occasionally recognition of the role of the natural variable in physical equations will permit more compact expression. For example, if one defines a natural variable equal to the ratio of the volume of a solid to the product of its length, depth, and breadth, one may then say that this variable has a value of unity for a cube or plinth (rectangular parallelepiped), $\pi/4$ for a right-circular or elliptical cylinder, and $\pi/6$ for a sphere or ellipsoid—and thereby gain some economy of expression. But beyond such small benefits the recognition of this property is of little importance in the formulation of relationships that are derived mathematically from fundamental laws.

8-7 The Form of Experimental Relations

Although a recognition of the basic properties of physical relations is not particularly important when a derivation can be accomplished, it becomes quite important when a derivation cannot be accomplished. Even when the fundamental laws that control the behavior of a physical system are known, the equation that describes the behavior may not always be available by the route of derivation. In many instances the system may be so complicated or the equations so unmanageable that the behavior is most easily deduced from experiment. But even though the result is arrived at without direct reference to the fundamental equations, it must still show the dimensional consistency that it would have acquired automatically if derived.

Since we know that any physical relation that conforms with known laws of nature may be expressed in terms of natural variables, we are supplied with a very simple scheme for ensuring dimensional consistency. Since a natural variable is dimensionless, any function of a natural variable will still be dimensionless. Therefore, if an experimental result is reported in terms of natural variables, it is automatically consistent dimensionally.

Because of the requirement of dimensional consistency, the way in which any particular physical variable enters a physical relation is not wholly independent of the way in which the other physical variables enter. We find, therefore, that if we impose the requirement of dimensional consistency on a physical relation we at the same time impose significant restrictions on the functional form of the relation—in other words, we learn a good deal about how the variables must be related before we ever run an experiment. Such information comes to us in a seemingly artificial way but is of course a natural contribution from the basic laws that relate the dimensions.

The nature of the information supplied may be seen from an example. The force on a sphere traveling through an incompressible fluid is dependent on the speed of travel V, the diameter of the sphere D, and the density and viscosity of the fluid ρ and μ; that is,

$$F = f(V,D,\rho,\mu) , \qquad (8\text{-}19)$$

where f means "function of." If we should proceed to find how F is dependent on each of the other variables, we would find that knowledge about one of the variables automatically yields a certain amount of information about the others. If, for example, we should find that F is directly proportional to μ, we could conclude immediately that ρ must have no influence on the force, since such a dependence would give inconsistency with regard to the force dimension. The force has the dimension F, and μ the dimensions FT/L^2; therefore ρ (with dimensions FT^2/L^4) could not appear in the relation without upsetting the existing consistency between the dimensions of F and μ. We could further conclude that the force must be proportional to V and to D to give consistency of length and time dimensions.

The conclusions we reach in this special case may be expressed more generally by writing Eq. (8-19) in terms of natural variables. Only two independent natural variables may be formed from the variables of Eq. (8-19). The dimensionless groups $F/\rho V^2 D^2$ and $\rho VD/\mu$ are a possible choice. We therefore conclude that in general Eq. (8-19) may take the form

$$\frac{F}{\rho V^2 D^2} = f\left(\frac{\rho VD}{\mu}\right). \qquad (8\text{-}20)$$

So we find that in general the functional relationship we seek by experiment may be arrived at by varying only one of the four independent substantial variables involved. If we found that F was proportional to μ, we would conclude from Eq. (8-20) that

$$\frac{F}{\rho V^2 D^2} = k\,\frac{\mu}{\rho VD}, \qquad (8\text{-}21)$$

where k is the constant of proportionality, or

$$F = k \cdot \rho V^2 D^2 \cdot \frac{\mu}{\rho VD} = k\mu VD, \qquad (8\text{-}22)$$

just as we concluded previously.

The form of a physical relation—as exemplified by Eq. (8-20)—depends directly on the relationships we admit among the dimensions involved. In writing Eq. (8-20) we have presumed that all the variables involved may be described in terms of dimensions of force, length, and time. In so doing we have implied that the following laws and definitions are pertinent to the physical behavior being described:

$$\rho = \frac{m}{s^3}, \qquad (8\text{-}23)$$

$$V = \frac{ds}{dt}, \qquad (8\text{-}24)$$

$$\tau = \mu \frac{dV}{ds}, \qquad (8\text{-}25)$$

$$\tau = \frac{F}{s^2}, \qquad (8\text{-}26)$$

$$F = \frac{d}{dt}(mV), \qquad (8\text{-}27)$$

where ρ = density,
m = mass,
s = distance,
V = velocity,
t = time,
τ = shear stress,
F = force.

The form of Eq. (8-20) is a subtle manifestation of these basic laws of nature. Newton's law [Eq. (8-27)]—along with Eqs. (8-23) and (8-24)—places restrictions on how force may be influenced by density, velocity, and diameter; the law of viscous shear [Eq. (8-25)]—along with Eq. (8-26)—places similar restrictions on how force may be influenced by viscosity, velocity, and diameter. These restrictions are implicit in Eq. (8-20).

A better understanding of how the fundamental laws exert an influence on the form of Eq. (8-20) is available if we consider how a modification in these laws affects the form of the equation. Such a demonstration also brings out clearly why dimensionally artificial statements of fundamental laws are improper.

Presumably Eq. (8-20) would not be essentially changed by including a dimensional physical constant in Newton's law. Equation (8-20) is the result of taking

$$F = ma \qquad (8\text{-}28)$$

as the standard form of Newton's law. If instead we had chosen to regard

$$F = m \frac{a}{g_c} \qquad (8\text{-}29)$$

as the standard form, then the dimensional physical constant g_c would have to be considered one of the variables of the problem. Instead of Eq. (8-20) we would get

$$\frac{F g_c}{\rho V^2 D^2} = f\left(\frac{\rho V D}{\mu g_c}\right). \qquad (8\text{-}30)$$

This equation clearly says exactly what Eq. (8-20) says; as we have already indicated, the specification that g_c is dimensionless is optional (conceptually).

On the other hand, if we should regard

$$F = m \frac{a}{g_o}, \qquad (8\text{-}31)$$

where g_o is the standard acceleration of gravity, as the proper statement of Newton's law, we would conclude that three independent natural variables could be formed. Equation (8-20) would then take a form such as

$$\frac{F g_o}{\rho V^2 D^2} = f\left(\frac{\rho V D}{\mu g_o}, \frac{V^2}{D g_o}\right). \qquad (8\text{-}32)$$

This is an essentially different result and is proper only when the acceleration that we have arbitrarily inserted in Newton's law is pertinent to the problem. The new variable introduced by this formulation of Newton's law is the square of Froude's number (for a standard gravitational field) and is properly included where standard gravity is influencing the flow; but it has no proper place in the relationship when gravity is not involved. We see, therefore, how an improper formulation of a fundamental relationship may throw a monkey wrench into the machinery of mathematical formulation.

More light is shone on the picture if we consider the special case of a flow in which Newton's law is not involved. The way in which we may introduce this idea varies depending on how we have chosen to write the fundamental law. If we are working with Newton's law in the form of Eq. (8-28), the obvious way to specify that Newton's law is not influential is to deny the relationship between the dimensions of force and mass provided by the law. We would then be forced to consider the variables of the problem describable in terms of four dimensions (F, M, L, T) rather than three. This would give dimensions of F to force, FT/L^2 to viscosity, and M/L^3 to density and would lead us to the conclusion that density could not enter the physical relation, since no other variable involves the dimension M. For dimensional consistency we would then conclude that the physical relation must take the form

$$\frac{F}{\mu VD} = \text{constant.} \qquad (8\text{-}33)$$

With the simpler framework of analysis occasioned by throwing out one of the fundamental laws, we come up with a simpler result. We might reach the same result by arguing that, if inertial effects are not important, density should drop out of the picture at the outset, since the influence of density depends on the influence of inertia. We may reach the same answer by dimensional reasoning or direct physical reasoning.

If Eq. (8-29) were regarded as the standard form of Newton's law, we would reach the same conclusion by a slightly different route. We could then argue that, if Newton's law is not involved, g_c should not be involved. Dropping g_c from the list of variables would immediately give Eq. (8-33). From a practical point of view, it is apparent that the presence of a physical constant in a fundamental law more clearly displays the influence of that law on the final formulation.

The addition of a fundamental influence may be handled in much the same way as the removal of an influence: either by considering what additional physical variable must enter, or by considering what additional relationship among dimensions must be admitted. As an example, if we felt that relativistic considerations should be involved, we could argue that the physical constant c (the free-space speed of light) should be regarded as one of the variables of the problem. We would then decide that

$$\frac{F}{\rho V^2 D^2} = f\left(\frac{\rho V D}{\mu}, \frac{V}{c}\right). \qquad (8\text{-}34)$$

Alternatively we could argue that, in the framework of relativity, length and time properly should be given the same dimension (that is, c should be regarded as dimensionless). Velocity would then become a natural variable, and we would conclude that

$$\frac{F}{\rho V^2 D^2} = f\left(\frac{\rho V D}{\mu}, V\right). \qquad (8\text{-}35)$$

Such an analysis gives us an unconventional form of equation, since the dimensional identity we have presumed is not recognized in the conventional relationships among units. For the sake of units we would therefore bow to convention and slip c into the equation as needed, giving us exactly Eq. (8-34).

Whether the influence of fundamental laws is introduced or rejected by introducing or rejecting appropriate physical variables or constants or by making appropriate changes in the dimensional system is unimportant; but the role of the fundamental laws either in suggesting the influence of the physical variable involved or in establishing the relationships among the dimensions involved must be recognized if an appropriate formulation is to be arrived at.

8-8 The Form of Incomplete Relations

It should not be inferred from the preceding remarks that we may express all physical relations in terms of natural variables. We may do so only if we know enough. If Newton's law and the shear law were unknown, Eq. (8-20) could obviously not be deduced. The best we could do would be to determine how force varies with diameter and velocity for a particular fluid (at a particular temperature and pressure). The relation would not involve natural variables, but it would of course—within its narrow confines—be entirely valid. A description in terms of natural variables is possible only when all the fundamental laws are known and reflected in the physical variables used to describe the situation. The natural variables then permit a generalization which would be unavailable otherwise.

It should not be imagined, however, that the expression in terms of natural variables is of value only if one is looking for the grand generalization. If one were interested in the force on spheres of different diameters in a specific fluid whose density and viscosity were fixed, one might be tempted to ignore the proprieties of physical description and proceed as if one were ignorant of the existence of density and viscosity. But Eq. (8-20) tells quite a bit about how the force is related to velocity and diameter, and it is folly to ignore it. One may easily see that, if ρ and μ are constant, F becomes a function of the product VD. The physical relation between F, V, and D may therefore be represented as a single curve of F versus VD rather than a family of curves of F versus V and D separately. The validity of such a representation is perhaps more obvious if Eq. (8-20) is rewritten in an equivalent form,

$$\frac{F}{\rho V^2 D^2}\left(\frac{\rho VD}{\mu}\right)^2 = f\left(\frac{\rho VD}{\mu}\right), \qquad (8\text{-}36)$$

which reduces to

$$F = \frac{\mu^2}{\rho} f\left(\frac{\rho VD}{\mu}\right). \qquad (8\text{-}37)$$

With ρ and μ constant this equation takes the form

$$F = f(VD). \qquad (8\text{-}38)$$

This same result could be reached in another fashion. We may argue that since ρ and μ are physical constants in the case at hand, there is no harm in considering them dimensionless. Mass would then merit the dimensions of length cubed, and force the dimensions of length squared over time. These relationships—along with the fact that F has the dimensions ML/T^2 by virtue of Newton's law—would then indicate that both F and VD are natural variables in this context and would lead at once to the writing of Eq. (8-38).

Problems and Examples

8-1. Check the following equations for dimensional consistency, and if possible indicate what variables might be lurking in the constant factors in the equations.

a. $P = \dfrac{TN}{5{,}250}$,

where P = power transmitted by a rotating shaft, hp,

T = torque, lb$_f$ft,

N = rotative speed, rpm.

b. $Q = 2.5H^{2.5}$,

where Q = flow rate over a triangular weir, ft^3/sec,

H = head, ft.

c. $C = \dfrac{7.354}{\log (s/r)} \cdot 10^{-9}$,

where C = capacitance of a transmission line to neutral, farads/1,000 ft,

s = spacing between lines, in.,

r = conductor radius, in.

8-2. The Napier rule for critical flow of steam through a nozzle is

$$m = \frac{pA}{70},$$

where m = flow rate, lb/sec,

p = absolute pressure, lb/in.^{2}

A = area, in.^{2}

Should the equation be expected to apply for the flow of air through a nozzle?

8-3. The capacitance C of a capacitor depends on its size L and on the permittivity of its dielectric material ϵ. In so far as its field is not confined to the dielectric, the capacitance also depends on the permittivity of the surrounding unpolarized medium ϵ_o. Based on a study of dimensions, determine (a) the dependence of C on L and ϵ when the leakage flux may be ignored; (b) the dependence of C on L, ϵ, and ϵ_o when it may not. What result is given by Gaussian dimensions, and to what situation does it apply?

8-4. One form of the relationship for convective heat transfer in a pipe is

$$\frac{hD}{k} = f\left(\frac{\rho V D}{\mu}, \frac{c\mu}{k}\right),$$

where h = heat-transfer coefficient,
$\quad\quad k$ = thermal conductivity,
$\quad\quad D$ = diameter,
$\quad\quad \rho$ = density,
$\quad\quad V$ = velocity,
$\quad\quad \mu$ = viscosity,
$\quad\quad c$ = specific heat.

What form would this equation take if inertia effects were unimportant?

Solution. The easiest way to answer this is to disqualify the relationship between mass and force dimensions. Since density and specific heat are the only variables that would then involve mass, the two numbers on the right-hand side would not be natural variables. Their product, however, would eliminate the mass dimension and make everything proper. Therefore the equation would take the form

$$\frac{hD}{k} = f\left(\frac{\rho V D}{\mu} \cdot \frac{c\mu}{k}\right) = f\left(\frac{\rho c V D}{k}\right).$$

8-5. The pressure drop in smooth, round pipes is usually described by the formula

$$\Delta p = f\frac{L}{D}\frac{1}{2}\rho V^2,$$

where f (the friction factor) is graphically presented as

a function of $\rho V D/\mu$. For a specific fluid (ρ and μ constant) what functional relationship exists among pressure drop per unit length $\Delta p/L$, mean velocity V, and diameter D?

9

Similitude

9-1 Introduction

Although we see that the rules for formulating physical behavior are simple once the underlying philosophy is recognized, conformance to the rules is not always so easy. If one can decide what substantial variables are involved in a problem and can decide what dimensional relationships are pertinent, then the problem of determining what natural variables are appropriate for describing the behavior is purely formal. But settling the initial question is often difficult. Fortunately we have in many situations a technique for discovering the natural variables that does not directly involve such decisions.

The technique involves a direct study of the equations from which the behavior of the system under consideration could be derived. What is needed essentially is the first step in the derivation—the statement of the equations and boundary conditions from which a derivation could theoretically be made. Usually such a statement will involve differential equations; however, knowledge of how to solve such differential equations is not required: all that is required is a knowledge of what equations are needed to define a solution.

The simplest information to extract from such equations is the requirement for similitude. Basically similitude is the condition of having the same shape or proportions, its most familiar usage being in the description of geometric figures. Similitude can therefore be defined as a condition in which the natural variables involved in a situation are fixed, since they are the parameters that describe shape or proportions. As a consequence, finding the requirement for similitude is synonymous with finding the natural variables definable for the system.

Although the term similitude is usually preferred, its dictionary synonym similarity is sometimes used in its place. Because of the absence of a satisfactory adjective form for similitude, the term similar usually fills that role.

9-2   Requirements Indicated by the Differential Equation

As an example of what differential equations reveal, we shall consider a specific problem: the two-dimensional flow of a viscous incompressible fluid past a circular cylinder. The equations satisfied by such a flow are the continuity equation, deriving from the idea of conservation of mass, and two momentum equations, deriving from Newton's law applied to the two coordinate directions:

$$\frac{\partial u}{\partial x} + \frac{\partial v}{\partial y} = 0, \tag{9-1}$$

$$\rho u \frac{\partial u}{\partial x} + \rho v \frac{\partial u}{\partial y} = -\frac{\partial p}{\partial x} + \mu \left(\frac{\partial^2 u}{\partial x^2} + \frac{\partial^2 u}{\partial y^2} \right), \tag{9-2}$$

$$\rho u \frac{\partial v}{\partial x} + \rho v \frac{\partial v}{\partial y} = -\frac{\partial p}{\partial y} + \mu \left(\frac{\partial^2 v}{\partial x^2} + \frac{\partial^2 v}{\partial y^2} \right). \tag{9-3}$$

The left-hand terms of the momentum equations represent inertia forces on a fluid particle (per unit volume); the right-hand terms, pressure forces and viscous forces, respectively. In these equations x and y are space coordinates in the direction of, and normal to, the flow at infinity, u and v are the corresponding velocity components, ρ is density, p is pressure, and μ is viscosity. The origin of the coordinate system is at the center of the cylinder. If the free-stream velocity is V, the cylinder diameter D, and the pressure at infinity p_∞, the boundary conditions may be written as follows:

At ∞:
$$u = V, \qquad v = 0, \qquad p = p_\infty. \tag{9-4}$$

At $x^2 + y^2 = \frac{1}{4}D^2$, the surface of the cylinder:
$$u = 0, \qquad v = 0. \tag{9-5}$$

In accepting these equations as adequate for defining the flow, we are making two assumptions that are perhaps not immediately obvious. We are first assuming that it is possible to establish a stable flow. We are also assuming that the flow established is not dependent on how the flow condition is approached; that is, that the previous history of the flow is not pertinent to its present circumstances. Although these assumptions may be expected to limit the scope of the analysis, they introduce no approximation within its range of application. We shall consider the limitations that they place on the analysis later.

The first question we may reasonably ask about flows described by these equations is what circumstance will give rise to identical flows. An inspection of the equations reveals that, if the fixed parameters V, D, p_∞, ρ, and μ are identical for two flows, all the equations we have written will also be identical. If we can assume that the flow is uniquely defined by the equations we have written, these five parameters are then the key to the character of the flow. We shall term them the characteristic parameters. The requirements for similitude are of course not so severe as the requirements for identity; however, they also involve the characteristic parameters.

Before arriving at a criterion for similitude for flows of this sort, it is necessary to have a clear notion of the meaning of similitude. Two flows are similar if one flow can be made identical to the other by the application of constant scale factors to each variable. In other words, if the coordinates of one flow are multiplied by a factor that makes the cylinder diameter the same, and if the velocities, the pressures, the density, and the viscosity are multiplied by factors that make the other characteristic parameters the same, then the two flows will be identical throughout, provided that they were similar to start with.

We usually think of similar systems as having the same geometry. Although geometrical similitude is a normal accompaniment of the similitude we seek, it is not an inevitable accompaniment. By applying different scale factors to the two coordinates (and to the corresponding velocity components) we might conceivably match the flow about an elliptical cylinder to flow about a circular cylinder. Systems that can be related in this manner are still regarded as similar, though often they are said to possess "distorted similitude." In most instances—and the present instance is no exception—similitude cannot be preserved without preserving the ratios between lengths or components; however, we shall eventually encounter examples where such a requirement need not be met.

The scale factors between the similar flows we are considering may be written as ratios of the characteristic parameters that we have identified. If two similar flows are denoted by primed and unprimed variables, respectively, then the scale factors between them may be written

$$\lambda_l = \frac{D'}{D} \qquad \text{length scale factor,} \qquad (9\text{-}6)$$

$$\lambda_v = \frac{V'}{V} \qquad \text{velocity scale factor,} \qquad (9\text{-}7)$$

$$\lambda_p = \frac{p'_\infty}{p_\infty} \qquad \text{pressure scale factor,} \qquad (9\text{-}8)$$

$$\lambda_\rho = \frac{\rho'}{\rho} \qquad \text{density scale factor,} \qquad (9\text{-}9)$$

$$\lambda_\mu = \frac{\mu'}{\mu} \qquad \text{viscosity scale factor.} \qquad (9\text{-}10)$$

With these factors defined, similitude can be described by saying that, if the velocities and pressure are u, v, and p at a point x, y in the first flow, they will be

$$u' = \lambda_v u, \qquad (9\text{-}11)$$
$$v' = \lambda_v v, \qquad (9\text{-}12)$$
$$p' = \lambda_p p, \qquad (9\text{-}13)$$

at a point in the second flow defined by

$$x' = \lambda_l x, \qquad (9\text{-}14)$$
$$y' = \lambda_l y. \qquad (9\text{-}15)$$

The density and viscosity inevitably follow similar relations, since they are assumed constant throughout:

$$\rho' = \lambda_\rho \rho, \qquad (9\text{-}16)$$
$$\mu' = \lambda_\mu \mu. \qquad (9\text{-}17)$$

The condition of similitude can be expressed in a somewhat different way that tends to emphasize the role of dimensionless variables. By combining Eqs. (9-6) through (9-8) with Eqs. (9-11) through (9-15), we may say that in the two similar flows

$$\frac{u'}{V'} = \frac{u}{V}, \tag{9-18}$$

$$\frac{v'}{V'} = \frac{v}{V}, \tag{9-19}$$

and

$$\frac{p'}{p'_\infty} = \frac{p}{p_\infty}, \tag{9-20}$$

at

$$\frac{x'}{D'} = \frac{x}{D}, \tag{9-21}$$

$$\frac{y'}{D'} = \frac{y}{D}. \tag{9-22}$$

In other words, if the variables of the problem are made dimensionless by dividing by the appropriate characteristic parameters, the flows, in terms of these dimensionless variables, are identical.

So far we have just looked at what similitude means; the next question is how to secure it for two different flows. The easiest approach to the answer is to substitute the variables of the first flow times the appropriate scale factors into the differential equations (and their boundary conditions) of the second. The resulting equations must then be compatible with the equations of the first flow. If we write Eqs. (9-1) through (9-5) in terms of the primed variables of the second flow and then substitute from Eqs. (9-11) through (9-17), we get the following set of equations:

$$\frac{\lambda_v}{\lambda_l}\left(\frac{\partial u}{\partial x} + \frac{\partial v}{\partial y}\right) = 0, \tag{9-23}$$

$$\frac{\lambda_\rho \lambda_v^2}{\lambda_l}\left(\rho u \frac{\partial u}{\partial x} + \rho v \frac{\partial u}{\partial y}\right) = -\frac{\lambda_p}{\lambda_l}\frac{\partial p}{\partial x} + \frac{\lambda_\mu \lambda_v}{\lambda_l^2}\mu\left(\frac{\partial^2 u}{\partial x^2} + \frac{\partial^2 u}{\partial y^2}\right), \tag{9-24}$$

$$\frac{\lambda_\rho \lambda_v^2}{\lambda_l} \left(\rho u \frac{\partial v}{\partial x} + \rho v \frac{\partial v}{\partial y} \right) = -\frac{\lambda_p}{\lambda_l} \frac{\partial p}{\partial y} + \frac{\lambda_\mu \lambda_v}{\lambda_l^2} \mu \left(\frac{\partial^2 v}{\partial x^2} + \frac{\partial^2 v}{\partial y^2} \right).$$
(9-25)

At ∞ :

$$\lambda_v u = \lambda_v V, \qquad \lambda_v v = 0. \qquad (9\text{-}26)$$

At $\lambda_l^2 x^2 + \lambda_l^2 y^2 = \lambda_l^2 \tfrac{1}{4} D^2$:

$$\lambda_v u = 0, \qquad \lambda_v v = 0. \qquad (9\text{-}27)$$

Except for Eqs. (9-24) and (9-25) these reduce exactly to Eqs. (9-1) to (9-5). Equation (9-24) may be written

$$\rho u \frac{\partial u}{\partial x} + \rho v \frac{\partial u}{\partial y} = -\frac{\lambda_p}{\lambda_\rho \lambda_v^2} \frac{\partial p}{\partial x} + \frac{\lambda_\mu}{\lambda_\rho \lambda_v \lambda_l} \mu \left(\frac{\partial^2 u}{\partial x^2} + \frac{\partial^2 u}{\partial y^2} \right)$$
(9-28)

and is seen to be the same as Eq. (9-2) except for the presence of two coefficients involving the λ's. The same relationship exists between Eqs. (9-25) and (9-3). For these new equations to be true, it is evident that the indicated coefficients must have a value of unity; that is,

$$\frac{\lambda_p}{\lambda_\rho \lambda_v^2} = 1, \qquad (9\text{-}29)$$

$$\frac{\lambda_\mu}{\lambda_\rho \lambda_v \lambda_l} = 1. \qquad (9\text{-}30)$$

If these requirements are met, the two flows are similar. We see that three of the characteristic parameters may be scaled arbitrarily (though not any three); the remaining two are then determined by this choice. If, for example, we changed the medium (hence ρ and μ) and the size, Eq. (9-30) would dictate the velocity necessary to give flow similitude and Eq. (9-29) the pressure.

The requirements indicated by Eqs. (9-29) and (9-30) can be rewritten in a more conventional form. If the

λ's are replaced by the ratios of characteristic variables [from Eqs. (9-6) through (9-10)], the relations indicated by Eqs. (9-29) and (9-30) can be expressed as

$$\frac{p'_\infty}{\rho'V'^2} = \frac{p_\infty}{\rho V^2},\tag{9-31}$$

$$\frac{\rho'V'D'}{\mu'} = \frac{\rho V D}{\mu}.\tag{9-32}$$

Thus similitude requires that two combinations of variables—which are seen to be dimensionless numbers formed from the characteristic parameters—must be the same. In conventional terms the first, $p_\infty/\rho V^2$, would be called a free-stream pressure coefficient and the second, $\rho V D/\mu$, a Reynolds number.

9-3   Interpretation of the Requirements

Anyone familiar with fluid mechanics might be wondering at this point whether we have made some horrible mistake. In flows of the sort considered in the last section it is well known that Reynolds number alone is ordinarily sufficient to ensure similitude; yet here we seem to have to worry about a pressure coefficient as well. It is a short-lived worry, however, if it is recognized that pressure level has no influence on this flow. What we have inadvertently done is ask for the similitude of the pressure when measured above an unspecified datum. Since we are still free to pick a datum, the pressure coefficient may be regarded as dictating what datum must be used. The obvious choice of datum is the pressure at infinity. With such a datum, p_∞ is zero and the number $p_\infty/\rho V^2$ automatically assumes the same value (zero) for all flows.

Setting up the equations in terms of a pressure referred to the pressure at infinity more clearly demonstrates the aptness of this pressure datum. Equations (9-1) to (9-5) may be written

$$\frac{\partial u}{\partial x} + \frac{\partial v}{\partial y} = 0, \tag{9-33}$$

$$\rho u \frac{\partial u}{\partial x} + \rho v \frac{\partial u}{\partial y} = -\frac{\partial (p - p_\infty)}{\partial x} + \mu \left(\frac{\partial^2 u}{\partial x^2} + \frac{\partial^2 u}{\partial y^2} \right), \tag{9-34}$$

$$\rho u \frac{\partial v}{\partial x} + \rho v \frac{\partial v}{\partial y} = -\frac{\partial (p - p_\infty)}{\partial y} + \mu \left(\frac{\partial^2 v}{\partial x^2} + \frac{\partial^2 v}{\partial y^2} \right). \tag{9-35}$$

At ∞:
$$u = V, \qquad v = 0, \qquad p - p_\infty = 0. \tag{9-36}$$

At the surface:
$$u = 0, \qquad v = 0. \tag{9-37}$$

Since the derivatives of p_∞ with respect to x and y are zero, these equations are reducible to their original form. In the present form, however, p_∞ does not appear as a characteristic parameter (provided that $p - p_\infty$, not p, is regarded as the pressure variable). The scale factor for pressure can therefore not be related to p_∞. It is evident, however, that the pressure difference must scale as ρV^2, particularly when it is considered that $\frac{1}{2}\rho V^2$ is the velocity pressure at infinity. Therefore, at corresponding points

$$p' - p'_\infty = \lambda_p (p - p_\infty), \tag{9-38}$$

where

$$\lambda_p = \frac{\rho' V'^2}{\rho V^2} = \lambda_\rho \lambda_v^2. \tag{9-39}$$

With this substitution, only the Reynolds number would appear as a requirement for similitude.

Another situation where an extraneous requirement seems to enter, only to be tossed out—or at least put in its proper place—after sober reflection, is the flow in which a gravitational field is present. If gravity acts in the $-y$ direction, the only significant change in the original equations is that Eq. (9-3) becomes

$$\rho u \frac{\partial v}{\partial x} + \rho v \frac{\partial v}{\partial y} = -\frac{\partial p}{\partial y} - \rho g + \mu \left(\frac{\partial^2 v}{\partial x^2} + \frac{\partial^2 v}{\partial y^2} \right),$$
(9-40)

where g is the acceleration of gravity. Following the same sort of analysis as before, we would find the additional requirement that

$$\frac{\lambda_g \lambda_l}{\lambda_v^2} = 1,$$
(9-41)

where

$$\lambda_g = \frac{g'}{g}.$$
(9-42)

Equation (9-41) may be rewritten as

$$\frac{V'}{\sqrt{D'g'}} = \frac{V}{\sqrt{Dg}}.$$
(9-43)

The dimensionless number $V/\sqrt{Dg}$ is called the Froude number.

The need for the Froude number as a criterion for similarity in this flow may be eliminated in much the same manner as the need for the pressure coefficient. The answer is again to refer the pressure to the pressure at infinity. In this case the pressure at infinity is variable:

$$p_\infty = \text{constant} - \rho g y.$$
(9-44)

Therefore, the derivatives of $p - p_\infty$,

$$\frac{\partial}{\partial x} (p - p_\infty) = \frac{\partial p}{\partial x},$$
(9-45)

$$\frac{\partial}{\partial y} (p - p_\infty) = \frac{\partial p}{\partial y} + \rho g,$$
(9-46)

bring forth the additional gravitational term needed. As a consequence, Eqs. (9-33) to (9-37) are valid even with gravity present, and no new restriction on similitude need appear.

Manipulations of this sort are permissible only because we have been willing to adjust our ideas of what constitutes similitude. If, for example, we were to demand that the pattern of absolute pressure possessed similitude, then the pressure coefficient would need to be reckoned with; with gravity present, similitude of the pressure measured above any fixed datum would require the same Froude number. But the similitude secured without concern for the pressure coefficient or Froude number is quite adequate, for pressure above any datum can be deduced from knowledge of $p - p_\infty$. It might be noted here, however, that similitude of $p - p_\infty$ (and velocity) may not secure a similitude of forces: with gravity present the cylinder will experience a buoyant force which will be in the same proportion to the horizontal force only if the Froude number is the same.

Where there is a free surface, the arguments that have virtually eliminated Froude number from the picture break down. At the free surface, pressure will be constant, which means that $p - p_\infty$ will not (unless the surface is undisturbed). If $p - p_\infty$ is used in the differential equations, Froude number will appear when the boundary condition at the free surface is inspected.

9-4   A Note about Turbulence

The equations treated have been written for a completely steady flow, thereby ruling out turbulence. Whether the appearance of turbulence in the flow will upset the previous conclusions is an important question.

To make the equations valid for a time-dependent phenomenon, only a small change is needed. The terms $\rho\, \partial u/\partial t$ and $\rho\, \partial v/\partial t$, respectively, must be added to the left-hand sides of the momentum equations. The boundary conditions may be retained as they were, for no turbulence would survive at infinity.

Although this small change renders the equations valid for a turbulent flow, the equations by themselves are no longer adequate for a unique description. The question of history becomes important; the exact nature of a turbulent flow at any moment depends on what its nature has been at previous moments. At the outset, therefore, we may appropriately ask only what are the conditions for similitude if the history of the flow has been similar.

We may answer this question by analyzing the altered equations as if they were adequate by themselves. Since the new variable time has appeared in the equations, a time scale factor now needs definition. For this purpose a characteristic time may be formed as D/V (which is the time for the fluid at infinity to move a distance equal to the cylinder diameter). The time scale factor between two similar flows therefore takes the form

$$\lambda_t = \frac{D'}{D} \cdot \frac{V}{V'} = \frac{\lambda_l}{\lambda_v}. \qquad (9\text{-}47)$$

Therefore, the relation between the time derivatives in two similar flows is

$$\rho' \frac{\partial u'}{\partial t'} = \frac{\lambda_\rho \lambda_v}{\lambda_t} \left(\rho\, \frac{\partial u}{\partial t} \right) = \frac{\lambda_\rho \lambda_v{}^2}{\lambda_l} \left(\rho\, \frac{\partial u}{\partial t} \right). \qquad (9\text{-}48)$$

We see by comparison with Eq. (9-24) that this relationship is the same as between the other inertial terms (such as $\rho u\, \partial u/\partial x$); therefore no new requirement appears. All that results is the conclusion that the time scale of fluctuations will be related to the length and velocity scales as indicated by Eq. (9-47).

In practice, of course, the coincidence of previous history is rare; the value of this conclusion may therefore seem negligible. It is usually found satisfactory, however, to regard the history of any turbulent flow as random and in this way define a unique turbulent condition that is independent of a detailed specification of history. The condition may be defined, however, only in terms of average behavior. We are therefore able to say that what would secure full similitude if the history is the same will secure similitude only of the average behavior if the history is random. Therefore, what normally is regarded as similarity in a turbulent flow, and the most that can ordinarily be hoped for, is a similarity of the patterns of the mean velocity and of the mean of the velocity fluctuations. If we accept this notion of similitude, no new parameter is introduced by turbulence.

The influence of history may not always be dismissed from the picture in this manner. Certain laminar flows, for example, may instead be turbulent if they have had a sufficiently disturbed history. Similitude of such metastable flows cannot be predicted or specified without in some way acknowledging the influence of previous experience in the present character of the flow.

It is important to note, for the sake of later considerations, that turbulence makes itself felt in the inertial terms of the momentum equations. If turbulence is present, the inertial terms are therefore important, even though the mean flow is unaccelerated.

The considerations that have been applied here to turbulence also apply to other time-varying flows. In particular, the time scale factor in similar transient flows will always be equal to the ratio of the length and velocity scales.

9-5   Dimensionless Differential Equations

Although working with scale factors sometimes has advantages, a slightly different approach in the study of differential equations is available which is normally more satisfactory. The essence of the approach is to rewrite the equations and boundary conditions in a dimensionless form. To accomplish this the variables of the problem are made dimensionless by use of the characteristic parameters. In the problem of flow past a cylinder we may define the following variables, all dimensionless, using the prime here to denote the dimensionless variables:

$$x' = \frac{x}{D}, \tag{9-49}$$

$$y' = \frac{y}{D}, \tag{9-50}$$

$$u' = \frac{u}{V}, \tag{9-51}$$

$$v' = \frac{v}{V}, \tag{9-52}$$

$$p' = \frac{p - p_\infty}{\rho V^2}. \tag{9-53}$$

(The last of these is defined in a manner that takes advantage of our previous enlightenment.) Expressed in terms of these variables, Eqs. (9-1) to (9-5) become

$$\frac{\partial u'}{\partial x'} + \frac{\partial v'}{\partial y'} = 0, \tag{9-54}$$

$$u' \frac{\partial u'}{\partial x'} + v' \frac{\partial u'}{\partial y'} = -\frac{\partial p'}{\partial x'} + \frac{\mu}{\rho V D} \left(\frac{\partial^2 u'}{\partial x'^2} + \frac{\partial^2 u'}{\partial y'^2} \right),$$

(9-55)

$$u' \frac{\partial u'}{\partial x'} + v' \frac{\partial v'}{\partial y'} = -\frac{\partial p'}{\partial y'} + \frac{\mu}{\rho V D} \left(\frac{\partial^2 v'}{\partial x'^2} + \frac{\partial^2 v'}{\partial y'^2} \right).$$

(9-56)

At ∞:

$$u' = 1, \qquad v' = 0, \qquad p' = 0. \qquad (9\text{-}57)$$

At $x'^2 + y'^2 = \frac{1}{4}$:

$$u' = 0, \qquad v' = 0. \qquad (9\text{-}58)$$

We see from these equations that all flows with the same Reynolds number, $\rho V D/\mu$, will obey identical equations in terms of these dimensionless variables and will therefore be similar.

With gravity in the picture the equations would be unchanged unless a disturbed free surface were present. In that event the Froude number would appear as a factor in the boundary condition at the free surface. The free surface would require the following:

At $y = y_s$:

$$p = p_s, \qquad (9\text{-}59)$$

where s denotes the surface. To find the boundary condition on $p - p_\infty$, we may note that

$$p_\infty = p_s + \rho g (y_o - y), \qquad (9\text{-}60)$$

where y_o is the undisturbed elevation of the surface, giving

$$p - p_\infty = p - p_s + \rho g (y - y_o). \qquad (9\text{-}61)$$

The surface boundary condition then becomes:

At $y = y_s$:

$$p - p_\infty = \rho g (y_s - y_o). \qquad (9\text{-}62)$$

In dimensionless form this becomes:

At $y' = y_s'$:

$$p' = \frac{Dg}{V^2} (y_s' - y_o').\tag{9-63}$$

The factor Dg/V^2 is recognized as the square of the reciprocal of Froude number.

9-6 Natural Units

The dimensionless version of an equation may be obtained directly by simply assuming that the variables in the ordinary equation are expressed in terms of a minimum number of natural units drawn from the characteristic parameters. If, for example, the characteristic parameters ρ, V, and D are selected as basic units, then the velocities u and v would have the natural unit V, the coordinates x and y would have the natural unit D, pressure would have the natural unit ρV^2, and viscosity would have the natural unit ρVD. The density would have the natural unit ρ and would therefore be unity. With these units the first momentum equation [Eq. (9-2)] would take the form

$$u' \frac{\partial u'}{\partial x'} + v' \frac{\partial u'}{\partial y'} = -\frac{\partial p'}{\partial x'} + \mu' \left(\frac{\partial^2 u'}{\partial x'^2} + \frac{\partial^2 u'}{\partial y'^2}\right),\tag{9-64}$$

in which primes are added to indicate that the variables are expressed in natural units (and therefore are really dimensionless variables). This equation is the same as Eq. (9-55), since

$$\mu' = \frac{\mu}{\rho VD}.\tag{9-65}$$

By this approach the Reynolds number appears as a dimensionless viscosity (or rather its reciprocal). More often one sees Eq. (9-64) written with ν' replacing μ'; but since $\nu' = \nu/VD$, where $\nu = \mu/\rho$, it amounts to the same thing.

This way of approaching the dimensionless form of the equation suggests at once that both constant parameters (ρ and μ) in the equation could be eliminated. If the basic natural units are taken as ρ, μ, and V, for example, ρ' and μ' will be unity and the equation will take the form

$$u' \frac{\partial u'}{\partial x'} + v' \frac{\partial u'}{\partial y'} = -\frac{\partial p'}{\partial x'} + \frac{\partial^2 u'}{\partial x'^2} + \frac{\partial^2 u'}{\partial y'^2}. \quad (9\text{-}66)$$

Here u', v', and p' would have natural units as before, but x' and y' would have the unit $\mu/\rho V$ and could be identified as

$$x' = \frac{\rho V x}{\mu}, \qquad y' = \frac{\rho V y}{\mu}, \quad (9\text{-}67)$$

in other words, as Reynolds numbers based on x and y. One could get the same equation [Eq. (9-66)] by using the natural units ρ, μ, and D. In that case u' and v' would be Reynolds numbers; p' would involve $\mu^2/\rho D^2$ as a natural unit. With the differential equation written in the form of Eq. (9-66), the requirement for similitude does not show up in the equation but appears in the boundary conditions instead.

9-7 Natural Similitude

Frequently a study of similitude reveals no requirement. In such cases similitude obtains independent of variation in the characteristic parameters. An instance of such natural similitude would occur in the flow problem we've treated if the fluid were inviscid. With the viscosity μ absent, the terms giving rise to Reynolds number in the differential equations would drop out.

Also no dimensionless group could be formed from the characteristic parameters. Thus all inviscid flows about the cylinder will display the same flow pattern.

For a weightless viscous fluid the density would drop out of the picture, and again give natural similitude. A flow of this sort is often called a slow flow, since the density and the accompanying inertia forces tend to become unimportant in most flows if the velocity is sufficiently decreased. In a slow flow the pressure would have to be expressed in terms of the natural unit $\mu V/D$ to display similarity; $(p - p_\infty)/\rho V^2$ would not follow the rule of similarity, since ρ is not among the characteristic parameters.

Though it doesn't affect the similitude argument, both these special cases require some alteration in boundary condition. For the inviscid flow, the boundary condition at the cylinder must be relaxed, only the radial component of velocity being made zero. For the slow flow, the infinity boundary cannot be met in this instance; in fact, the cylinder proves too much of an obstruction, and the only steady solution available gives zero velocity everywhere; but the natural similitude argument is valid for other instances where slow flow is realized.

9-8   Similitude and Physical Description

The parameters that establish similitude are synonymous with the independent natural variables that enter a physical relation, provided that the nature of the similitude and the nature of the relation correspond. As we have seen, only one parameter, the Reynolds number, is needed to ensure similitude of velocity, even though there may be gravity acting (provided that the free surface is undisturbed). Therefore any dimensionless velocity or flow function will be a function of only this one variable. An unperceptive analysis of the equations might easily have deceived one into thinking that the Froude number and perhaps even the pressure coefficient should also be added to the list of natural variables; and as we have seen, they are proper natural variables in answer to some questions—though we have also seen that the questions aren't really proper. The equations, in other words, give the answer to the question asked, but they don't reveal that the question asked may be a poor one. In the original formulation we effectively asked under what circumstances the pattern of velocity and absolute pressure would be unchanged; and we got an obedient and correct answer. It was only after recognizing that this was a rather stupid question that we got the answer we really wanted. A study of the equations, therefore, is a sure technique for discovering the natural variables involved, but one has to be careful to recognize just what it is they are involved in.

The notion of similitude permits the nature of physical relations to be regarded in a somewhat different light. Because of the fact of similitude, the whole behavior of a physical system may be envisaged as a succession of similar states, each of which represents a range of conditions. Describing the behavior is then just a matter of establishing the succession of similar states, which amounts to establishing how the dimensionless variables that describe these states are related. The similitude itself is a manifestation of an underlying law of behavior: two different states show a similarity because they are both influenced by the same fundamental laws.

Problems and Examples

9-1. The response of a d-c motor may be approximately described by the following equations:

$$V = IR + L\frac{dI}{dt} + k_e\omega,$$

$$k_tI = J\frac{d\omega}{dt},$$

where V = applied voltage,

$\quad I$ = current,

$\quad R$ = resistance,

$\quad L$ = inductance,

$\quad t$ = time,

$\quad k_e$ = speed-voltage constant (voltage per unit speed),

$\quad \omega$ = angular speed,

$\quad k_t$ = torque constant (torque per unit current),

$\quad J$ = moment of inertia.

a. What are the requirements for similitude of response to a constant applied voltage?

b. What moment of inertia would be required by a model to give a response similar to a prototype?

c. How will the time scale and speed scale of the model compare with the prototype?

Solution.   *a.* It is a simple matter to deceive oneself in this problem. To demonstrate how it may happen, we shall proceed in a manner that gives rise to a deception. The dependent variables of the problem are I and/or ω, which are functions of the independent variable t. The characteristic parameters that determine the nature of these functions are V, R, L, k_e, k_t, and J. An obvious way to make I dimensionless is by use of V/R, which has the dimensions of current; and an obvious way to make ω and t dimensionless is by use of L/R, which has the dimensions of time. If these are used, we get

$$1 = I' + \frac{dI'}{dt'} + \frac{k_e R}{LV} \omega',$$

$$I' = \frac{JR^3}{k_t VL^2} \frac{d\omega'}{dt'},$$

where $I' = \dfrac{I}{V/R}$,

$$\omega' = \frac{\omega}{R/L},$$

$$t' = \frac{t}{L/R}.$$

These equations suggest that two dimensionless parameters ($k_e R/LV$ and $JR^3/k_t VL^2$) must be equated to secure similitude—but it's a delusion. Both parameters multiply the same variable (ω'), and one of them may be eliminated by redefining that variable.

If we let

$$\omega'' = \frac{k_e R}{LV} \omega' = \frac{\omega}{V/k_e},$$

which is just as good a dimensionless description of ω, we get

$$1 = I' + \frac{dI'}{dt'} + \omega'',$$

$$I' = \frac{JR^2}{k_e k_t L} \frac{d\omega''}{dt'},$$

and find that only one dimensionless parameter is needed.

By inspecting the original formulation we see that we inadvertently imposed a relationship between ω and t by referring them to the same parameter. With the reference used, $\omega t = \omega' t'$, so that similitude involved equality of ωt at corresponding times. In other words, we were asking under what conditions the response of two systems will be similar at the same values of ωt (that is, the same number of revolutions of the motor). This additional restriction is obviously not desired.

This problem happens to be one that may (in its stated form) be solved analytically without much trouble. The analytical solution is

$$I = \frac{V}{R\sqrt{1 - 4\delta}} \, (e^{-at} - e^{-bt}),$$

where $a = \dfrac{R}{2L} (1 + \sqrt{1 - 4\delta})$,

$$b = \frac{R}{2L} (1 - \sqrt{1 - 4\delta}),$$

$$\delta = k_e k_t L / J R^2.$$

This may be rewritten dimensionlessly as

$$I' = \frac{1}{\sqrt{1 - 4\delta}} \, (e^{-\alpha t'} - e^{-\beta t'}),$$

where $\alpha = \frac{1}{2}(1 + \sqrt{1 - 4\delta})$,
$\beta = \frac{1}{2}(1 - \sqrt{1 - 4\delta})$,

If δ, which is the inverse of the parameter just found, is made the same, α and β will also be the same; then I' as a function of t' will be identical. This problem is reconsidered from the dimensional viewpoint in Prob. 11-1.

   b. To make the parameter $JR^2/k_e k_t L$ the same, the model moment of inertia will have to be

$$J = J' \left(\frac{R'}{R}\right)^2 \left(\frac{k_e}{k_e'}\right) \left(\frac{k_t}{k_t'}\right) \left(\frac{L}{L'}\right),$$

where prime refers to prototype and no prime to model.
   c. Since the dimensionless time will be the same,

corresponding times will be in the ratio of the respective values of L/R. By similar arguments speeds will be in the ratio of respective values of V/k_e.

9-2. If there is an electric field strength of value $E_x = E_o \sin \omega t$ at the surface of a semi-infinite conductor, the solution within the conductor may be determined from the differential equation

$$\frac{\partial^2 E_x}{\partial z^2} = \mu\sigma \frac{\partial E_x}{\partial t},$$

where x = coordinate along surface,

$\quad z$ = coordinate normal to surface (inward),

$\quad \omega$ = circular frequency (2π times frequency),

$\quad t$ = time,

$\quad \mu$ = magnetic permeability,

$\quad \sigma$ = electrical conductivity.

$\quad a.$ How may the condition of similitude be expressed?

$\quad b.$ How may it be secured?

$\quad c.$ How is the selected characteristic length related to the so-called depth of penetration $(\pi f\mu\sigma)^{-\frac{1}{2}}$, where f = frequency? (The depth of penetration is the point where E_x drops to $1/e$ of its surface value.)

9-3. If the physical variable A of a particular system were found to depend on the variables B and C in the following manners, what conclusions about similitude are suggested?

$\quad a.$ $A = f(B,C)$.

$\quad b.$ $A = f(BC)$.

$\quad c.$ $A =$ constant BC.

9-4. If a homogeneous sphere initially at uniform temperature is immersed in fluid of different temperature, the temperatures at points within the sphere will vary with time in a manner dependent on the coefficient of heat transfer to the ambient fluid and the thermal properties of the sphere. The differential equation describing the temperature within the sphere is

$$\frac{\partial T}{\partial t} = \alpha \left(\frac{\partial^2 T}{\partial x^2} + \frac{\partial^2 T}{\partial y^2} + \frac{\partial^2 T}{\partial z^2} \right).$$

The initial condition is

$$T = T_b \qquad \text{at } t = 0.$$

The boundary condition is

$$k \frac{\partial T}{\partial r} = h(T_a - T) \qquad \text{at } r = R.$$

In these equations

$$\begin{aligned}
r &= \text{radial position in sphere,} \\
x, y, z &= \text{cartesian coordinates,} \\
t &= \text{time,} \\
T &= \text{temperature at point } r, \\
T_b &= \text{initial uniform temperature of sphere,} \\
T_a &= \text{constant ambient temperature,} \\
\alpha &= k/\rho c = \text{thermal diffusivity,} \\
k &= \text{thermal conductivity of sphere,} \\
\rho &= \text{density of sphere,} \\
c &= \text{specific heat of sphere,} \\
h &= \text{surface heat-transfer coefficient.}
\end{aligned}$$

a. How may similarity of temperature be described?

b. How may it be secured?

9-5. If a uniform cantilever is subjected to a lateral force F at the free end, its deflection may be determined from the equation

$$EI \frac{d^2 y}{dx^2} = F(L - x),$$

where E = modulus of elasticity,

$$\begin{aligned}
I &= \text{cross-sectional moment of inertia,} \\
y &= \text{deflection,} \\
x &= \text{distance from fixed end,} \\
L &= \text{length.}
\end{aligned}$$

If the same beam is permitted to vibrate freely, its deflection may be determined from the equation

$$EI \frac{\partial^4 y}{\partial x^4} = -\mu \frac{\partial^2 y}{\partial t^2},$$

where μ = mass per unit length,
t = time.

Consider such a beam to be deflected a distance δ at the free end and then released.

a. Show that, if the scale factors or dimensionless variables are appropriately defined, the initial deflection curves and subsequent vibration curves of such beams will possess natural similitude.

b. Is there any inherent defect or approximation in a "distorted model"—that is, a model in which distances are scaled differently in different directions?

10
Dimensionless Relations

10-1 Introduction

From the last two chapters it is evident that there are two basic approaches to setting up the dimensionless relations that provide a framework for describing the behavior of a system. One approach is to study the general equations that control the behavior of the system. How these equations exert influence is most easily detected by looking at the dimensions of the variables, with the result that the approach takes on the guise of a study of dimensions. The other approach is to study the specific equations that control the behavior of the system. How these equations exert influence is most easily detected by looking at the requirements for similitude, with the result that the approach takes on the guise of a study of models. Despite the conventionally different overtones, however, both approaches arrive at the same conclusions. In this chapter we shall compare the results obtained by the two approaches.

Besides alternative ways to find the dimensionless relations that form the framework of physical description, there are alternative ways to express these rela-

156

tions once they are found. Some of the considerations involved in selecting the proper form are discussed later in the chapter.

10-2 Relations Obtained from Similitude

The conspicuous result obtained from our study of the differential equations of the last chapter was the requirement for similitude. Interpreted narrowly, this result indicates the circumstances under which the performance of a particular system may be predicted from the performance of a model. Specifically, it was found that, if a model was operated at the same Reynolds number, it would have the same pattern of velocity as the prototype. This similarity of behavior can be described mathematically by saying that for either the prototype or its model the velocities may be described dimensionlessly by the same functions:

$$\frac{u}{V} = f_1\left(\frac{x}{D}, \frac{y}{D}\right), \tag{10-1}$$

$$\frac{v}{V} = f_2\left(\frac{x}{D}, \frac{y}{D}\right). \tag{10-2}$$

Thus, if we can find u and v as a function of x and y for the model, we can at once deduce u and v as a function of x and y for the prototype, if operated at the same Reynolds number.

The truth implicit in these conclusions, however, need not be bound up in the idea of a model and a prototype or restrained by the notion of similitude. We are also in a position to compare behavior at different Reynolds numbers—that is, at nonsimilar conditions. Evidently, for states that are not similar the velocities must be describable by relations of the form

$$\frac{u}{V} = f_1 \left(\frac{x}{D}, \frac{y}{D}, \frac{\rho V D}{\mu} \right),\qquad(10\text{-}3)$$

$$\frac{v}{V} = f_2 \left(\frac{x}{D}, \frac{y}{D}, \frac{\rho V D}{\mu} \right).\qquad(10\text{-}4)$$

If Reynolds number is constant, these equations reduce to the form of Eqs. (10-1) and (10-2). The general dimensionless relationship among the variables is always directly obtainable by adding the dimensionless variables that establish similitude to the dimensionless variables that describe it. The conclusions of similitude, therefore, though seemingly quite restricted, are in fact a sufficient basis for writing the general equations that relate the natural variables.

Similar arguments can be made to get the dimensionless relation for the pressure field. Before worrying about the significance of pressure level, we argued that p/p_∞ would be the same function of x/D and y/D if $p_\infty/\rho V^2$ and $\rho V D/\mu$ were the same. In general, then, we could argue that the pressure could be expressed by a relation of the form

$$\frac{p}{p_\infty} = f \left(\frac{x}{D}, \frac{y}{D}, \frac{p_\infty}{\rho V^2}, \frac{\rho V D}{\mu} \right).\qquad(10\text{-}5)$$

Similarly, the enlightened conclusion that $(p - p_\infty)/\rho V^2$ would be the same function of x/D and y/D, with only $\rho V D/\mu$ the same, leads to the conclusion that

$$\frac{p - p_\infty}{\rho V^2} = f \left(\frac{x}{D}, \frac{y}{D}, \frac{\rho V D}{\mu} \right).\qquad(10\text{-}6)$$

It is interesting to note that, if we start with Eq. (10-5) and consider what form it must take to be insensitive to pressure level, we arrive directly at Eq. (10-6). The latter equation is a specialized form of Eq. (10-5), a fact more apparent if it is rearranged to read

$$\frac{p}{p_\infty} = 1 + \frac{\rho V^2}{p_\infty} f\left(\frac{x}{D}, \frac{y}{D}, \frac{\rho V D}{\mu}\right). \qquad (10\text{-}7)$$

Although these examples have involved parameters that are variable at a state of similitude, the same arguments also apply to parameters that are constant at a state of similitude. A parameter—such as a force coefficient for the cylinder—that is constant when similitude obtains normally becomes a function of Reynolds number when similitude is departed from.

10-3 Relations Obtained from Dimensional Analysis

The direct use of dimensional analysis arrives at these same equations. Without any prior consideration of similitude one may conclude that the velocity components u and v should depend on location x, y and on the value of the characteristic parameters V, D, ρ, μ; that is,

$$u, v = f(x,y,V,D,\rho,\mu). \qquad (10\text{-}8)$$

(An abbreviated notation is used in this equation. The variables u and v are each functions of the same variables, but the functions are not necessarily the same.) With a small amount of study we may conclude that the dimensionless equation

$$\frac{u}{V}, \frac{v}{V} = f\left(\frac{x}{D}, \frac{y}{D}, \frac{\rho V D}{\mu}\right) \qquad (10\text{-}9)$$

represents the most general form that Eq. (10-8) can take and still retain dimensional compatibility. [An organized technique for going from Eq. (10-8) to Eq. (10-9) is explained in the next chapter.] We therefore come immediately to the conclusions stated in Eqs. (10-3) and (10-4).

By similar reasoning, the supposition that

$$p = f(x,y,V,D,\rho,\mu,p_\infty) \tag{10-10}$$

would lead immediately to the conclusion that

$$\frac{p}{p_\infty} = f\left(\frac{x}{D}, \frac{y}{D}, \frac{\rho VD}{\mu}, \frac{p_\infty}{\rho V^2}\right); \tag{10-11}$$

and the supposition that

$$p - p_\infty = f(x,y,V,D,\rho,\mu) \tag{10-12}$$

would lead immediately to the conclusion that

$$\frac{p - p_\infty}{\rho V^2} = f\left(\frac{x}{D}, \frac{y}{D}, \frac{\rho VD}{\mu}\right). \tag{10-13}$$

The requirements for similitude may, of course, be deduced directly from the equations obtained in this way. Equations (10-9) and (10-13) indicate that for u/V, v/V, or $(p - p_\infty)/\rho V^2$ to be the same functions of x/D and y/D requires only that $\rho VD/\mu$ be the same.

Dimensional analysis quickly provides other answers that might be a chore to extract from the differential equations. An example is the proper relationship for the force F on the cylinder (per unit length). By dimensional reasoning we would argue that, since

$$F = f(V,D,\rho,\mu), \tag{10-14}$$

it follows that

$$\frac{F}{\rho V^2 D} = f\left(\frac{\rho VD}{\mu}\right). \tag{10-15}$$

We thus at once find that, if we define an appropriate force coefficient, it will be a function of Reynolds number alone. To extract the same information from the differential equations would involve setting up the pressure and shear integrals that evaluate the force and studying them; it would hardly be termed an immense job, but it would certainly be an unnecessary one in a situation such as this where the variables involved are well understood.

10-4   The Form of Dimensionless Relations

Often there is a choice in the form a dimensionless relation may take. Usually the best choice is indicated by considering some limiting or special case of the problem. As an example, the dimensionless expression for force on the cylinder was written

$$\frac{F}{\rho V^2 D} = f\left(\frac{\rho V D}{\mu}\right). \qquad (10\text{-}16)$$

It could as legitimately have been written

$$\frac{F}{\mu V} = f\left(\frac{\rho V D}{\mu}\right). \qquad (10\text{-}17)$$

Which form should be preferred?

The answer should probably depend on the limiting flow of most interest. One limit is flow at very high Reynolds number. Here the magnitude of μ becomes unimportant; the equations must therefore reduce to a form that shows no influence of μ on F. Equation (10-16) reduces to

$$\frac{F}{\rho V^2 D} = \text{constant}, \qquad (10\text{-}18)$$

whereas Eq. (10-17) would become

$$\frac{F}{\mu V} = \frac{\rho V D}{\mu} \cdot \text{constant}. \qquad (10\text{-}19)$$

Clearly the first force coefficient is better for expressing this limit.

On the other hand, at very low Reynolds number the density ρ ordinarily has no influence. At this limit the equations would then reduce to

$$\frac{F}{\rho V^2 D} = \frac{\mu}{\rho V D} \cdot \text{constant} \qquad (10\text{-}20)$$

and

$$\frac{F}{\mu V} = \text{constant.} \qquad (10\text{-}21)$$

Were this limit of most interest, the latter coefficient would be the logical choice.

Usually overruling considerations of logic, however, are the considerations of convention. It has become an almost universal practice to define force and stress coefficients in terms of density rather than viscosity, even though density may not properly enter the problem. Such conventions can often create confusion; one can easily deceive oneself about similitude if the dimensionless groups used are arbitrarily brought into the problem rather than originating there. If one considers the usual force coefficient in a slow flow, for example, one finds that it varies inversely with Reynolds number [Eq. (10-20)]. Finding Reynolds number in the picture, one might almost be forgiven for concluding that the flow must be one that requires equality of Reynolds number for similitude; but of course it isn't.

10-5   The Tyranny of Custom

Custom not only results in the appearance of dimensionless numbers in places where they don't logically belong: it also may dictate an awkward form of a dimensionless relation, simply for the sake of expressing it in terms of familiar numbers. A good example is the conventional representation of flowmeter characteristics. The usual scheme for a meter that measures the pressure drop across an obstruction such as that created by a nozzle is to plot a meter coefficient which refers the flow to some sort of ideal flow (for example, to the flow that might ideally be expected from the measured pressure drop) as a function of a Reynolds number. A typical form is

$$\frac{Q}{A\sqrt{2\,\Delta p/\rho}} = f\left(\frac{\rho QD}{\mu A}\right), \qquad (10\text{-}22)$$

where Q = volume flow rate,
     p = measured pressure drop,
  A, D = area and diameter of nozzle,
  ρ, μ = density and viscosity.

The flow-nozzle characteristic may be presented as a plot of the flow coefficient represented by the left-hand term as a function of the Reynolds number represented by the right-hand term (which is a Reynolds number based on the mean velocity discharging from the nozzle).

The awkward feature of such a representation is that the usual problem must be solved by trial and error. Normally one measures the pressure drop and wishes to find the flow rate; but the representation of Eq. (10-22) puts flow rate in both terms, making direct calculation impossible.

The possibility of eliminating Q from one of the terms is obvious. If Eq. (10-22) is true, it is also true that

$$\frac{Q}{A\sqrt{2\,\Delta p/\rho}} = f\left(\frac{\rho QD}{\mu A} \cdot \frac{A\sqrt{2\,\Delta p/\rho}}{Q}\right)$$

$$= f\left(\frac{\rho D\sqrt{2\,\Delta p/\rho}}{\mu}\right). \qquad (10\text{-}23)$$

In this form the right-hand term can be calculated directly. The new term may be interpreted, if desired, as a Reynolds number based on the theoretical velocity that entered the definition of the flow coefficient.

Problems and Examples

10-1. If a sphere having a constant uniform surface temperature is traveling through a fluid having constant dynamic and thermal properties, the heat-transfer rate Q from the sphere will be a function of the following variables:

$$Q = f(\Delta T, V, D, \rho, \mu, c, k),$$

where ΔT = difference in temperature between sphere surface and undisturbed fluid,

V = velocity of travel,

D = diameter,

ρ = density,

μ = viscosity,

c = specific heat,

k = thermal conductivity.

From dimensional reasoning one would deduce that this equation may take the form

$$\frac{hD}{k} = f\left(\frac{\rho V D}{\mu}, \frac{c\mu}{k}, \frac{c\,\Delta T}{V^2}\right),$$

where

$$h = \frac{Q}{\pi D^2\,\Delta T} = \text{surface heat-transfer coefficient.}$$

a. Show that the last term of this correlation drops out if viscous dissipation has negligible influence.

b. Show that, if the last term is present, the form of the correlation is unsatisfactory.

c. What form will the correlation take if heat transfer is a linear function of temperature difference at any particular flow condition?

Solution.   *a.* The correlation presented makes use of the concept that heat and mechanical energy have the same dimensions. If the warming effect of viscous action is presumed negligible, however, the appropriate dimensional picture is one that does not identify heat and mechanical energy. The thermal variables would then have the dimensions $H/TL^2\theta$ for h, $H/TL\theta$ for k, and $H/M\theta$ for c, where H = heat, T = time, L = length, θ = temperature, M = mass. The heat dimension drops out of all terms except the last, where an identification of heat with $FL = ML^2/T^2$ is needed to eliminate it. Therefore without this identification only the first three terms are properly present in the correlation.

b. If the last term cannot be discarded by such arguments, the four terms provide a correct framework for correlation, but an extremely awkward one. The difficulty is that Q will in general be finite when ΔT is zero, making the left-hand term infinite at such a point. This situation may be cured by rewriting the equation as

or

$$\frac{hD}{k} \cdot \frac{c\,\Delta T}{V^2} = f\left(\frac{\rho VD}{\mu}, \frac{c\mu}{k}, \frac{c\,\Delta T}{V^2}\right)$$

$$\frac{Qc}{\pi k V^2} = f\left(\frac{\rho VD}{\mu}, \frac{c\mu}{k}, \frac{c\,\Delta T}{V^2}\right).$$

This form gives no quirk at ΔT of zero.

c. If it can be argued that Q should be a linear function of ΔT when the other parameters are fixed, then the correlation would be written

$$\frac{Qc}{\pi k V^2} = f_1\left(\frac{\rho VD}{\mu}, \frac{c\mu}{k}\right) + \frac{c\,\Delta T}{V^2} f_2\left(\frac{\rho VD}{\mu}, \frac{c\mu}{k}\right)$$

This may be written in a somewhat handier form if we define ΔT_o as the temperature difference when Q is zero. Then

$$0 = f_1 + \frac{c\,\Delta T_o}{V^2} f_2,$$

which permits the correlation to be written

$$\frac{Qc}{\pi k V^2} = -\frac{c\,\Delta T_o}{V^2} f_2 + \frac{c\,\Delta T}{V^2} f_2 = \frac{c(\Delta T - \Delta T_o)}{V^2} f_2$$

or

$$\frac{Q}{\pi k(\Delta T - \Delta T_o)} = f_2\left(\frac{\rho V D}{\mu}, \frac{c\mu}{k}\right),$$

where ΔT_o is determined from

$$\frac{c\,\Delta T_o}{V^2} = -\frac{f_1}{f_2} = f_3\left(\frac{\rho V D}{\mu}, \frac{c\mu}{k}\right).$$

We may now reasonably define a new heat-transfer coefficient

$$h_e = \frac{Q}{\pi D^2(\Delta T - \Delta T_o)},$$

which is the heat transfer per unit area per unit of temperature measured above the temperature that gives no heat flow (rather than above the ambient). This definition permits the correlation to be written

$$\frac{h_e D}{k} = f_2\left(\frac{\rho V D}{\mu}, \frac{c\mu}{k}\right)$$

in a form matching the correlation involving no dissipation.

Conventionally the equation for ΔT_o is written with a factor of 2 in the left-hand term:

$$\frac{\Delta T_o}{V^2/2c} = f_4\left(\frac{\rho V D}{\mu}, \frac{c\mu}{k}\right).$$

The term so defined is called the recovery factor (a nomenclature that makes some sense in a compressible flow, but not much here).

10-2. By dimensional reasoning one may deduce that the velocity of small-amplitude waves on the surface of a liquid may be described by an equation of the following form, if the influence of viscosity is small:

$$\frac{V^2}{\lambda g} = f\left(\frac{\lambda}{h}, \frac{\rho V^2 \lambda}{\sigma}\right),$$

where V = wave velocity,
   λ = wavelength,
   g = acceleration of gravity,
   h = depth of liquid,
   ρ = density,
   σ = surface tension.

a. If the wavelength is long compared with depth, the velocity is substantially independent of wavelength. What form does the relationship take under such circumstances? If surface tension is uninfluential, what is the dependence of velocity on depth?

b. If the wavelength is short compared with depth, the velocity is substantially independent of depth. What form does the relationship take under such circumstances? If surface tension is uninfluential, what is the dependence of velocity on wavelength? If gravity is uninfluential, what is the dependence of velocity on wavelength? What parameter indicates the relative importance of surface tension and gravity?

10-3. Pressure-drop data for pipes are usually presented on a plot of friction factor f versus Reynolds number $\rho V D/\mu$ and relative roughness ϵ/D, where

$$f = \frac{\Delta p}{\frac{1}{2}\rho V^2}\frac{D}{L},$$

ρ = density,
μ = viscosity,
V = mean velocity,
D = diameter,
L = length,
ϵ = a length characteristic of roughness.

How could such information be presented to make the calculation of mean velocity from knowledge of the pressure drop a simpler job?

11

The Technique of
Dimensional Analysis

11-1 Introduction

Many, if not most, dimensional analyses are so simple that no particular technique is needed to discover the dimensionless numbers involved once the pertinent variables and dimensions are recognized. Occasionally, however, there may be a question whether any number has been overlooked. It is therefore handy to have an infallible technique that will reveal all the necessary numbers automatically. Of the various techniques available, the one presented here seems the easiest and surest.

11-2 The Step-by-step Approach

The step-by-step approach is effectively just an organized technique based on the notion of natural units. The easiest description of the approach is by an example. The problem of the force on the cylinder considered in the last chapter (Sec. 10-3) provides a satisfactory example. We start again with the supposition that

168

$$F = f(\rho, V, D, \mu). \qquad (11\text{-}1)$$

The variables present have the following dimensions:

$$F \qquad \frac{F}{L} = \frac{M}{T^2}$$

$$\rho \qquad \frac{M}{L^3}$$

$$V \qquad \frac{L}{T}$$

$$D \qquad L$$

$$\mu \qquad \frac{M}{LT}$$

The procedure is now to rid the equation of each dimension in turn. If, for example, we divide F and μ by ρ, giving

$$\frac{F}{\rho} = f\left(\rho, V, D, \frac{\mu}{\rho}\right), \qquad (11\text{-}2)$$

we have eliminated the dimension M from all terms except ρ itself. The new equation is clearly just as general as the old. We now observe, however, that ρ cannot have a proper place in the new equation since it is the only term involving the mass dimension. Therefore it follows that

$$\frac{F}{\rho} = f\left(V, D, \frac{\mu}{\rho}\right). \qquad (11\text{-}3)$$

We may now, in analogous fashion, use V to eliminate the time dimension:

$$\frac{F}{\rho V^2} = f\left(V, D, \frac{\mu}{\rho V}\right) = f\left(D, \frac{\mu}{\rho V}\right). \qquad (11\text{-}4)$$

Finally we use D to eliminate the length dimension:

$$\frac{F}{\rho V^2 D} = f\left(D, \frac{\mu}{\rho V D}\right) = f\left(\frac{\mu}{\rho V D}\right). \qquad (11\text{-}5)$$

Equation (11-5) is of course tantamount to

$$\frac{F}{\rho V^2 D} = f\left(\frac{\rho V D}{\mu}\right), \qquad (11\text{-}6)$$

the equation we wrote previously [Eq. (10-15)].

Interpreting the technique in terms of natural units, we see that we have successively called on ρ, V, and D to fill this role. We have found in the end that the remaining parameters, F and μ, may then be expressed in units of $\rho V^2 D$ and $\rho V D$, respectively.

The example presented may be somewhat misleading in that each dimension was eliminated by use of one of the original variables. The fact that the variables used for this purpose happened to be the original variables was accidental; the circumstance that made them usable was their appearance in the previous step. The general technique is probably more clearly demonstrated by starting off in a different way. If the length dimension is eliminated first by use of D, we get from this first step

$$FD = f\left(\rho D^3, \frac{V}{D}, \mu D\right). \qquad (11\text{-}7)$$

The respective terms here have dimensions M/T^2, M, $1/T$, and M/T. The time dimension may now be eliminated by use of any one of the three terms involving time. The most obvious choice is V/D, the second term on the right. This step gives

$$\frac{FD^2}{V^2} = f\left(\rho D^3, \frac{\mu D^2}{V}\right). \qquad (11\text{-}8)$$

The terms now all have the dimension M. Using ρD^3 to eliminate that dimension, we get the previous result:

$$\frac{F}{\rho V^2 D} = f\left(\frac{\mu}{\rho V D}\right). \qquad (11\text{-}9)$$

11-3   The Buckingham Pi Theorem

The Buckingham pi theorem is a rule for deciding how many dimensionless numbers (called π's in Buckingham's notation) to expect. The theorem is of no value if the step-by-step approach is used, nor is it even much help if the intuitive approach is used. But the theorem is of interest for the reason that reputedly drives the mountain climber to the summit: it's there.

The theorem states that the number of independent dimensionless groups is equal to the difference between the number of variables that go to make them up and the number of independent dimensions involved. The weakness of the theorem—from a practical point of view—is that it does not depend on the number of dimensions actually used, but rather on the minimum number that might have been used. In the example, we started with five variables (F, ρ, V, D, and μ) which involved three dimensions. Two dimensionless groups resulted, just as Buckingham would want. About all we may conclude from this, however, is that the dimensions involved cannot be combined in some way to give less than three dimensions.

The workings of the rule are quite clear from the step-by-step approach. In each step of the approach, one dimension is eliminated and the number of variables is reduced by one. Therefore the total reduction in number of variables must equal the total number of dimensions. The only hitch is that one step of the process may occasionally eliminate two of the dimensions at once, thereby resulting in one more dimensionless number than expected. In situations where this happens it can be shown that a smaller number of dimensions could have been used to describe the variables.

If we consider the heat transfer from the cylinder that we have been analyzing, we can get into a situation of this sort. The average heat-transfer coefficient h for the cylinder will depend on the flow parameters V, D, ρ, and μ and also on the thermal conductivity k and thermal capacity c_p of the fluid. Straightforward analysis would show these variables to be related as

$$\frac{hD}{k} = f\left(\frac{\rho VD}{\mu}, \frac{c_p\mu}{k}\right). \qquad (11\text{-}10)$$

But straightforward analysis doesn't reveal what we are looking for; with seven variables and four dimensions (the fourth being θ, the temperature), we would expect, and get, three dimensionless ratios.

A slightly different approach is available, however. The variables ρ and V appear in the result only as a product; had the mass velocity $G = \rho V$ been considered a characteristic parameter, rather than ρ and V separately, the same answer should result. (Whether this is a reasonable starting point is not an issue in the present discussion.) We would start then with the supposition that

$$h = f(G, c_p, \mu, k, D), \qquad (11\text{-}11)$$

with dimensions (shown in both force and mass equivalents):

$$h \qquad \frac{F}{TL\theta} = \frac{M}{T^3\theta}$$

$$G \qquad \frac{FT}{L^3} = \frac{M}{L^2T}$$

$$c_p \qquad \frac{L^2}{T^2\theta} = \frac{L^2}{T^2\theta}$$

$$\mu \qquad \frac{FT}{L^2} = \frac{M}{LT}$$

$$k \qquad \frac{F}{T\theta} = \frac{ML}{T^3\theta}$$

$$D \qquad L = L$$

We may now eliminate the mass (or force) dimension by dividing appropriately by G:

$$\frac{h}{G} = f\left(G, c_p, \frac{\mu}{G}, \frac{k}{G}, D\right) = f\left(c_p, \frac{\mu}{G}, \frac{k}{G}, D\right) \cdot \quad (11\text{-}12)$$

The temperature dimension may be eliminated through use of c_p:

$$\frac{h}{c_p G} = f\left(c_p, \frac{\mu}{G}, \frac{k}{c_p G}, D\right) = f\left(\frac{\mu}{G}, \frac{k}{c_p G}, D\right) \cdot \quad (11\text{-}13)$$

If we now seek to eliminate the time dimension, we find we're too late: it dropped out with the temperature dimension. Elimination of the length dimension then gives the dimensionless form

$$\frac{h}{c_p G} = f\left(\frac{\mu}{GD}, \frac{k}{c_p GD}, D\right) = f\left(\frac{\mu}{GD}, \frac{k}{c_p GD}\right) \cdot \quad (11\text{-}14)$$

This may not look exactly like Eq. (11-10), but if we recognize that

$$\frac{h}{c_p G} = \frac{hD}{k} \cdot \frac{\mu}{GD} \cdot \frac{k}{c_p \mu}, \qquad (11\text{-}15)$$

$$\frac{k}{c_p GD} = \frac{k}{c_p \mu} \cdot \frac{\mu}{GD}, \qquad (11\text{-}16)$$

we see that it's equivalent.

Since we started with six variables and four dimensions but found three, rather than two, dimensionless ratios, the Buckingham pi theorem says we could have gotten by with only three dimensions to define the variables. Since it was $T^2\theta$ that dropped out in the second step, we would expect this might be one of the three. Another two can easily be selected by inspection:

$$h \qquad \frac{(FT)}{(T^2\theta)L} = \frac{(M/T)}{(T^2\theta)}$$

$$G \qquad \frac{(FT)}{L^3} = \frac{(M/T)}{L^2}$$

$$c_p \qquad \frac{L^2}{(T^2\theta)} = \frac{L^2}{(T^2\theta)}$$

$$\mu \qquad \frac{(FT)}{L^2} = \frac{(M/T)}{L}$$

$$k \qquad \frac{(FT)}{(T^2\theta)} = \frac{(M/T)L}{(T^2\theta)}$$

$$D \qquad L = L$$

We find then that the three dimensions FT, $T^2\theta$, and L, or M/T, $T^2\theta$, and L, would have done the job and given the proper Buckingham answer.

The Buckingham pi theorem, if applied to the actual number of dimensions being used, tells only that there must be at least a certain number of dimensionless numbers involved. Unless one resorts to one of the tedious techniques that have been devised for discovering the minimum number of dimensions needed, the theorem gives little assurance that all the dimensionless numbers have been found—an assurance that can very quickly be secured from the step-by-step approach, if assurance is needed.

11-4 The Problems and Pitfalls of Dimensional Analysis

It can easily be recognized that acquisition of the bare technique of dimensional analysis is no problem;

the real problems come before and after the crank is turned. One must first decide what variables enter the problem. If the problem is not well enough understood to make this initial choice clear, the dimensional analysis will seldom provide clarification. Occasionally a dimensional analysis will show that one of the selected variables should not be present, since it involves a dimension not shared by any of the other variables (a circumstance that could also arise if a needed variable had been left out); but such perception is usually not to be expected of a dimensional analysis: if the wrong variables go in, the wrong dimensionless numbers come out, most of the time.

One error to avoid in choosing the variables is the inclusion of variables whose influence is already implicitly accounted for. In analyzing the dynamics of a liquid flow, for example, one might argue that the liquid temperature is a significant variable. It is important, however, only in its influence on other properties such as viscosity, and should therefore not be included along with them.

Once the pertinent variables are determined, there is still the question of the proper dimensional picture for them. In many situations the conventional dimensions provide this picture; however, occasionally some of the ideas implicit in the conventional dimensions are inappropriate. The dimensions deserve more attention than they usually get; the implications of a dimensional picture are not always obvious (as the first of the problems at the end of the chapter demonstrates).

Because of the subtle considerations involved in dimensional analysis, a seemingly proper analysis sometimes gives rise to extraneous dimensionless numbers. If no rules have been broken—if subtleties have merely been overlooked—the result of such an analysis is in-

correct only in that it is overcomplicated or overrestric-
tive. In other words, the analysis is correct as far as
it has gone: it simply hasn't gone as far as it ought to go.
Viewed in the context of similitude, the error in such an
analysis can be interpreted as inadvertently asking for
more similitude than desired. The possibility of extraneous numbers coming out of a dimensional analysis
makes it advisable to study the result closely to see if
it makes sense. For this study a knowledge of what
sort of numbers to expect and how to interpret them
is valuable. The next chapter considers this question.

Problems and Examples

11-1. Solve Prob. 9-1 by dimensional analysis.

Solution. The current in the circuit will be a function of the six constant parameters plus time:

$$I = f(V,R,L,k_e,k_t,J,t).$$

These variables have the following dimensions:

I	I
V	V
K	$\dfrac{V}{I}$
L	$\dfrac{VT}{I}$
k_e	VT
k_t	$\dfrac{FL}{I}$
J	$ML^2 = FLT^2$
t	T

Defined in this manner, the parameters involve effectively four dimensions: I, V, T, and FL. One is tempted
to identify FL with VIT (corresponding mechanical and

electrical dimensions of work or energy), thereby reducing the number of dimensions to three; however, such an identification is inappropriate because the function as set up does not depend on the existence of a relationship between mechanical and electrical energies.

Since there are eight parameters and four dimensions, the pi theorem would suggest that four π's are involved —and we may easily see here that no reduction of dimensions is possible. By inspection we may arrive at the dimensionless relation

$$\frac{I}{V/R} = f\left(\frac{t}{L/R}, \frac{JR^3}{k_t VL^2}, \frac{k_e R}{LV}\right).$$

To secure similitude of I versus t, therefore, we appear to need two parameters—the same two that we discovered in the initial analysis of Prob. 9-1.

Here again a subtle defect may be discerned in the analysis—a defect analogous to the one that upset the original formulation. As it enters the problem, angle, or rotation, is not properly regarded as a dimensionless idea. By assigning it no dimensions in setting up the dimensions of k_e and J one inadvertently gives it a meaning that is inappropriate to the present description. If one assigns a dimension (A) to angle, then the dimension of J is FLT^2/A and of k_e, VT/A. This gives each of the last two terms of the correlation the dimension $1/A$. To render the correlation dimensionless, therefore, it is necessary to replace them by their ratio, giving

$$\frac{I}{V/R} = f\left(\frac{t}{L/R}, \frac{JR^2}{k_e k_t L}\right),$$

which checks the previous result.

The full implication of this change in viewpoint can be seen from looking at the corresponding equation for angle of the rotor. With angle regarded as dimensionless, it would be related in the same way as any other dimensionless dependent variable:

$$\alpha = \omega t = f\left(\frac{t}{L/R}, \frac{JR^3}{k_t V L}, \frac{k_e R}{LV}\right).$$

Regarded as dimensional, it would instead enter a relationship such as

$$\frac{\alpha}{LV/k_e R} = f\left(\frac{t}{L/R}, \frac{JR^2}{k_e k_t L}\right).$$

The first equation indicates that at a condition of similitude α will be the same function of dimensionless time; the second equation does not make this same contention. So in effect the initial approach unconsciously demanded a fuller similitude than was desired.

11-2. In a Saybolt Universal viscosimeter the time for a specified amount of liquid to drain through a tube in the bottom of a cylindrical container is measured.

a. Demonstrate that for such an instrument the time of efflux t is a function only of the kinematic viscosity ν if the size and gravitational field are fixed.

b. The following numerical equation gives a good approximation of ν in centistokes as a function of t in seconds for t between 50 and 100 sec:

$$\nu = 0.220t - \frac{195}{t}.$$

Generalize this equation to show the influence of size and gravitational acceleration.

c. If a liquid gave a reading of 50 sec on earth, what reading would it give on a planet where the gravitational acceleration is half as much?

Solution.   *a.* Since the viscosity, inertia, and weight of the fluid are all involved, the time will be a function of viscosity, density, acceleration of gravity (or specific weight), and size:

$$t = f(\mu,\rho,g,L).$$

Using ρ, g, and L successively to eliminate M, T, and L dimensions, one gets

$$\frac{t}{\sqrt{L/g}} = f\left(\frac{\mu}{\rho\sqrt{gL^3}}\right) = f\left(\frac{\nu}{\sqrt{gL^3}}\right).$$

Therefore, if g and L are fixed, t is a function of ν alone.

b. The dimensionless form that will give rise to the quoted equation if L and g are fixed is clearly

$$\frac{\nu}{\sqrt{gL^3}} = c_1\frac{t}{\sqrt{L/g}} + c_2\frac{\sqrt{L/g}}{t}$$

or

$$\nu = c_1gLt + c_2\frac{L^2}{t}.$$

If L_o and g_o are the values of L and g for which the quoted constants hold, we may write the equation as

$$\nu = 0.220\left(\frac{g}{g_o}\frac{L}{L_o}\right)t - 195\left(\frac{L}{L_o}\right)^2\frac{1}{t}$$

(a numerical equation).

c. For $L = L_o$, $g = g_o$, and $t = 50$, ν comes out 7.10 (centipoises). Therefore, if g is half of g_o,

$$7.10 = 0.220(\tfrac{1}{2})t - 195\frac{1}{t},$$

from which $t = 85.4$ sec.

11-3. a. Solve Prob. 9-4 by dimensional analysis.

b. If the conductivity of the sphere varies with temperature according to the relationship

$$k = k_a[1 + \beta_a(T_a - T)],$$

what parameters are needed to secure similitude?

11-4. Demonstrate by dimensional analysis that the stress at corresponding points in similar rotating disks made of the same material is the same if the peripheral speed is the same.

11-5. A conceivable scheme for measuring the rate of heat transfer between a droplet of liquid and a gas through which it is moving is to measure the frequency of its vibration. At the instant of formation droplets are somewhat nonspherical, and the action of surface tension tending to make the drop spherical coupled with the inertia of the fluid will normally set up a vibration of droplet shape. Measurement of the frequency of this vibration and the size of the droplet plus knowledge of how the liquid properties vary with temperature should give an indication of droplet temperature.

Show by dimensional analysis how the frequency depends on the parameters involved, considering damping to be small.

11-6. By the mixing-length theory the shear stress in a turbulent pipe flow may be expressed

$$\tau = \rho l^2 \left(\frac{dV}{dy}\right)^2,$$

where ρ = density,
V = velocity,
y = transverse coordinate,
l = mixing length.

By the Kármán hypothesis l at any point is a function of the local velocity derivatives. If it is presumed to be a function of the first two velocity derivatives, one may express it as

$$l = k \frac{dV/dy}{d^2V/dy^2},$$

where k is a dimensionless constant. The form of this equation suggests that if l is presumed to be a function of the first three velocity derivatives it might be expressed as

$$l = k_1 \frac{dV/dy}{d^2V/dy^2} + k_2 \frac{d^2V/dy^2}{d^3V/dy^3},$$

where k_1 and k_2 are dimensionless constants.

a. Is the first equation for l the most general that can be written if l is assumed to be a function of the first two velocity derivatives?

b. Is the second equation for l the most general that can be written if l is assumed to be a function of the first three velocity derivatives?

12

Dimensionless Numbers
and Their Interpretation

12-1 Introduction

Given enough time, one can usually decide what dimensionless numbers are available for the description of a physical situation from a study of the equations or variables involved. But time is often saved and analysis made more certain if one has some idea what to expect. It is valuable, for example, to know when the Reynolds number will come into a flow problem and when it will not. By an adequate understanding of the significance of the various dimensionless numbers one can often decide immediately the form that a dimensionless relation will take. Also one can check the result of one's analysis to see if the numbers that have appeared make sense.

The material in this chapter serves to reveal and interpret the more commonly encountered numbers of fluid mechanics and heat transfer. It is also intended to serve as a guide to the sort of thinking that may be useful in interpreting other dimensionless numbers. The

182

chapter also includes several examples of dimensional and differential-equation studies.

12-2   The Dependent Variables of Fluid Dynamics

A large number of dimensionless variables have come into being for the sake of describing the dynamical behavior of fluids. The usual substantial variables for describing behavior are velocities, pressures, shear stresses, or forces. It is common practice, where possible, to make these variables dimensionless by use of a characteristic velocity, density, and length or area. A dimensionless velocity may be formed by dividing by V, a dimensionless pressure or shear stress by dividing by ρV^2, and a dimensionless force by dividing by $\rho V^2 L^2$ or $\rho V^2 A$.

By custom a factor of $\frac{1}{2}$ is normally inserted before ρV^2 in those dimensionless numbers where it appears. The term $\frac{1}{2}\rho V^2$, commonly called the dynamic pressure, can be interpreted as the velocity pressure in an incompressible flow. A typical pressure coefficient therefore takes the form

$$C_p = \frac{p - p_\infty}{\frac{1}{2}\rho V^2}. \tag{12-1}$$

Similarly, a force coefficient (such as lift or drag coefficient) will normally be expressed

$$C_F = \frac{F}{\frac{1}{2}\rho V^2 A}. \tag{12-2}$$

By the usual convention the area appearing in the latter expression is the frontal area for a bluff body such as a sphere, the plan area for a lifting device.

A pressure coefficient of a special sort is the friction factor, which is a dimensionless pressure drop per unit length in a pipe. The pressure drop per unit length

$\Delta p/L$ is made dimensionless by use of $\frac{1}{2}\rho V^2$ (where V is mean flow velocity) and the diameter D:

$$f = \frac{\Delta p/L}{\frac{1}{2}\rho V^2/D} = \frac{\Delta p}{\frac{1}{2}\rho V^2} \cdot \frac{D}{L}. \qquad (12\text{-}3)$$

Some choose to define friction factor in terms of wall shear stress τ_o, following the customary rule for making stress dimensionless:

$$f' = \frac{\tau_o}{\frac{1}{2}\rho V^2}. \qquad (12\text{-}4)$$

Unfortunately, the two factors turn out to be different by a constant factor: the first is four times the second.

Where velocity is not present as a characteristic variable, its role is sometimes played by the combination $(2\,\Delta p/\rho)^{1/2}$, which can be identified as the velocity that would give rise to a dynamic pressure of Δp. Thus a flow coefficient for a nozzle or the like may (as in Sec. 10-5) be defined

$$C = \frac{Q}{A\sqrt{2\,\Delta p/\rho}}, \qquad (12\text{-}5)$$

where Q is volume flow rate and A exit area.

Some of the dimensionless performance parameters one encounters can be interpreted as ratios of actual performance to some arbitrary ideal performance. The denominator of Eq. (12-5), for example, is the ideal incompressible flow through a nozzle of discharge area A if the discharge velocity profile is uniform and the upstream velocity negligible. Thus the flow coefficient C, being a ratio of actual flow to an ideal flow, can be regarded as a sort of correction factor. Different selections of the ideal may often give rise to different dimensionless numbers for the same use: for example, a slightly different flow coefficient is frequently defined in which upstream velocity is taken into account in the ideal flow. In cases where a dimensionless number of this sort can be interpreted as an energy or power ratio, it is quite often termed an efficiency. The efficiency of a nozzle, for example, is usually defined as the ratio of actual kinetic-energy change in the nozzle to the ideal that might be achieved with the same pressure drop. Use of the term efficiency in this sense has caused some confusion, since many people come out of childhood equipped with the notion that efficiency is always a ratio of output to input, where in fact it is more often a ratio of the actual to the ideal, or the reverse. Although efficiencies of this sort are of some value as measures of merit, they owe their existence, or at least their usefulness, mainly to the fact that they are dimensionless expressions of performance.

12-3   Reynolds Number

Reynolds number, the most familiar independent parameter of fluid mechanics, is usually written in one of the following three forms:

$$\frac{\rho V L}{\mu} = \frac{V L}{\nu} = \frac{G L}{\mu}, \qquad (12\text{-}6)$$

where ρ = density,
  V = a velocity,
  L = a length,
  μ = viscosity,
  ν = kinematic viscosity (μ/ρ),
  G = mass velocity (ρV).

It is usually interpreted as the ratio of the inertia forces to the viscous forces in a flow. How this interpretation arises is easily seen from the problem of flow past a cylinder considered previously. The left-hand terms of Eq. (9-2) [and (9-3)] represent the inertia force on a fluid element (per unit volume). For similar flows these terms will evidently be proportional to the characteristic parameters in the following manner:

$$\rho u \frac{\partial u}{\partial x} + \rho v \frac{\partial u}{\partial y} \sim \frac{\rho V^2}{D} . \tag{12-7}$$

The viscous term will obey a similar proportionality:

$$\mu \left(\frac{\partial^2 u}{\partial x^2} + \frac{\partial^2 u}{\partial y^2} \right) \sim \frac{\mu V}{D^2} . \tag{12-8}$$

The ratio of these terms gives the Reynolds number:

$$\frac{\rho V^2 / D}{\mu V / D^2} = \frac{\rho V D}{\mu} . \tag{12-9}$$

All that this manipulation says for sure is that in similar flows involving Reynolds number the ratio of inertia to viscous forces will be the same at corresponding points. But it also tempts one to conclude that the influence of inertia forces will become greater at high Reynolds number and the influence of viscous forces greater at low Reynolds number. Support of these conclusions is available from many flows. As an example, for flow in a straight pipe of finite roughness the pressure drop at sufficiently low Reynolds number is proportional to viscosity and not influenced by inertia forces, while at sufficiently high Reynolds number it is proportional to density and not influenced by viscous forces. But, on the other hand, a perfectly smooth pipe, if it could be found, would show a continuing influence of viscosity at high Reynolds number, since viscous forces would continue to be predominant in the flow immediately adjacent to the wall. The size of the Reynolds number will be an accurate measure of the proportionality of inertia to viscous forces only if the flow pattern doesn't change; but since a change in

Reynolds number often means a change in flow pattern, its value as such a measure may be spurious.

One can safely say only that if viscous and inertia forces are involved, so is Reynolds number. To go on to say that its magnitude is indicative of the relative importance of inertia and viscous forces is too frequently folly. It would seem safe enough to conclude, however, that, if inertia forces become predominant at a particular Reynolds number, they will retain their dominance at all higher Reynolds numbers or that, if viscous forces swamp the inertia forces at one Reynolds number, they will do so at all lower values.

12-4 Froude Number

The Froude number is normally written as

$$\frac{V}{\sqrt{Lg}}, \qquad (12\text{-}10)$$

where V = a velocity,
L = a length,
g = acceleration of gravity.

Like Reynolds number it may be related to the ratio of two terms of the momentum equation. The ratio of the inertia force on a fluid element and the gravity force turns out to be proportional to the square of the Froude number. (Probably for this reason, the square of the number defined here is sometimes considered the Froude number.) In Eq. (12-7) the inertia force is found proportional to $\rho V^2/D$. The gravity force [see Eq. (9-40)] is ρg and is already in terms of characteristic variables. Therefore

$$\frac{\text{Inertia force}}{\text{Gravity force}} \sim \frac{\rho V^2/D}{\rho g} = \frac{V^2}{Dg}, \qquad (12\text{-}11)$$

which is a Froude number squared.

As already demonstrated, the Froude number comes into prominence in flow with a free surface. It is particularly associated with gravity waves, which involve an interaction between gravity and inertia forces. As also demonstrated, an incompressible flow without a free surface need not involve Froude number if properly treated. One would expect, on the other hand, that any compressible flow would, since the technique that separated the gravitational effects in an incompressible flow would not work for a compressible one. In most cases, however, it is possible to ignore the Froude number in a compressible flow because of the relative smallness of gravitational influence. A possible exception to this conclusion occurs in any flow in which free convection (a convection maintained by gravitational forces) is important. As indicated later, however, the Froude number is not usually called on to describe this influence.

12-5   Weber Number

The Weber number is another number that may be involved when a free surface exists. Its usual form is

$$\frac{\rho V^2 L}{\sigma}, \tag{12-12}$$

where ρ = density,
   V = velocity,
   L = length,
   σ = surface tension (which has the form of force per unit length).

Weber number is proportional to the ratio of inertia force to surface-tension force, as shown by the following argument: The pressure difference across a curved surface is equal to the surface tension σ over the radius of curvature R (an appropriate mean radius if the surface curves both directions); therefore, the pressure difference across the free surface of a flow is

$$\Delta p_{\text{surface}} = \frac{\sigma}{R} \sim \frac{\sigma}{L}. \qquad (12\text{-}13)$$

The inertial pressure difference within the fluid is seen from Eq. (9-2) to have the form

$$\Delta p_{\text{inertia}} \sim \left(\rho u \frac{\partial u}{\partial x} + \rho v \frac{\partial u}{\partial y} \right) \Delta x \sim \rho V^2. \quad (12\text{-}14)$$

The ratio of (12-14) to (12-13) gives the Weber number:

$$\frac{\Delta p_{\text{inertia}}}{\Delta p_{\text{surface}}} \sim \frac{\rho V^2}{\sigma/L} = \frac{\rho V^2 L}{\sigma}. \qquad (12\text{-}15)$$

Weber number, like Froude number, is apt to be associated with waves; where Froude number is associated with gravity waves, Weber number is associated with surface-tension waves, which involve interaction between inertia and surface forces.

12-6 Ideal Compressible Flow

If a flow is compressible, several additional dimensionless variables make their appearance. The most familiar of these is the Mach number. The Mach number does not come into the picture in an obvious way, nor does it come alone. To discover its origin and assist its interpretation, therefore—as well as to see what else is involved—we may appropriately look at the details of a particular compressible flow. We shall look again at the flow past a cylinder but this time admit compressibility—that is, variable density.

Since the problem of a viscous compressible flow is rather complicated, an inviscid flow will be considered first. The viscosity and thermal conductivity will both be considered zero. For such a flow the entropy of the fluid is constant, and the density may be expressed as a function of pressure alone. The pressure-density relationship may be written in a number of different ways. A satisfactory method for our purposes is to make use of the adiabatic exponent γ, which is defined as

$$\gamma = \frac{\rho}{p}\left(\frac{\partial p}{\partial \rho}\right)_s, \qquad (12\text{-}16)$$

where the subscript s denotes constant entropy. With entropy constant, this definition reduces to

$$\frac{dp}{p} = \gamma\,\frac{d\rho}{\rho}. \qquad (12\text{-}17)$$

For γ constant, this expression yields the familiar isentropic equation of state

$$\frac{p}{\rho^\gamma} = \text{constant}; \qquad (12\text{-}18)$$

but in general γ may vary. In addition to Eq. (12-17) we need the continuity equation, which for a compressible flow relates mass-velocity derivatives rather than simply velocity derivatives (as for an incompressible flow):

$$\frac{\partial}{\partial x}(\rho u) + \frac{\partial}{\partial y}(\rho v) = 0. \qquad (12\text{-}19)$$

The momentum equations are also needed, which for inviscid flow are the same as for incompressible:

$$\rho u\,\frac{\partial u}{\partial x} + \rho v\,\frac{\partial u}{\partial y} = -\frac{\partial p}{\partial x}, \qquad (12\text{-}20)$$

$$\rho u\,\frac{\partial v}{\partial x} + \rho v\,\frac{\partial v}{\partial y} = -\frac{\partial p}{\partial y}. \qquad (12\text{-}21)$$

As boundary conditions we have:
At ∞ :

$$u = V, \quad v = 0, \quad p = p_\infty, \quad \rho = \rho_\infty. \qquad (12\text{-}22)$$

The boundary condition at the cylinder merely states that the radial velocity component is zero.

Dimensionless variables may be defined much as for the incompressible flow:

$$p' = \frac{p - p_\infty}{\rho_\infty V^2}, \qquad (12\text{-}23)$$

$$\rho' = \frac{\rho}{\rho_\infty}, \qquad (12\text{-}24)$$

$$u' = \frac{u}{V}, \qquad (12\text{-}25)$$

$$v' = \frac{v}{V}, \qquad (12\text{-}26)$$

$$x' = \frac{x}{D}, \qquad (12\text{-}27)$$

$$y' = \frac{y}{D}. \qquad (12\text{-}28)$$

The variable γ is already dimensionless. With these variables we may rewrite the equations in the following dimensionless form:

$$\frac{dp'}{p' + p_\infty/\rho_\infty V^2} = \frac{\gamma \, d\rho'}{\rho'}, \qquad (12\text{-}29)$$

$$\frac{\partial}{\partial x'}(\rho' u') + \frac{\partial}{\partial y'}(\rho' v') = 0, \qquad (12\text{-}30)$$

$$\rho' u' \frac{\partial u'}{\partial x'} + \rho' v' \frac{\partial u'}{\partial y'} = -\frac{\partial p'}{\partial x'}, \qquad (12\text{-}31)$$

$$\rho' u' \frac{\partial v'}{\partial x'} + \rho' v' \frac{\partial v'}{\partial y'} = -\frac{\partial p'}{\partial y'}. \qquad (12\text{-}32)$$

At ∞:

$$u' = 1, \quad v' = 0, \quad p' = 0, \quad \rho' = 1. \quad (12\text{-}33)$$

The only equation that places any limitations on similitude is Eq. (12-29). For this equation to be the same for two systems, the parameter $p_\infty/\rho_\infty V^2$ and the adiabatic exponent γ must be the same. The exponent need not be a constant; but if it varies, it should be the same function of p' and ρ'. With $p_\infty/\rho_\infty V^2$ the same, this is equivalent to saying that γ must be the same function of p/p_∞ and ρ/ρ_∞. For many gases γ depends predominantly on molecular structure and does not vary greatly with pressure or density, so that the restriction on γ often amounts to saying that similitude requires the fluid to have a similar molecular structure; for example, most diatomic-gas flows would be expected to satisfy this similitude requirement approximately.

The requirement on $p_\infty/\rho_\infty V^2$ is conventionally expressed in a different way. It can be shown that the speed of sound (which is defined as the speed of propagation of a small isentropic disturbance in the fluid) is expressible as

$$a = \sqrt{\frac{\gamma p}{\rho}}. \tag{12-34}$$

We may then write the reciprocal of $p_\infty/\rho_\infty V^2$ as

$$\frac{\rho_\infty V^2}{p_\infty} = \gamma_\infty \left(\frac{V}{a_\infty}\right)^2. \tag{12-35}$$

The dimensionless ratio V/a_∞ is the Mach number of the free stream. Therefore, similitude may alternatively be assured by requiring the free-stream Mach number to be the same, and the adiabatic exponent γ to be the same function of p/p_∞ and ρ/ρ_∞.

One is tempted to try to interpret Mach number in terms of forces, as with other dimensionless flow parameters. Those who yield to this temptation usually regard Mach number as the square root of the ratio of inertia force and "elastic force." Since there is no separate term in the force equations that might be identified as an "elastic term," an interpretation of Mach number that exactly parallels the usual interpretation of Reynolds or Froude number would appear improper. One can, however—perhaps a bit loosely—interpret Mach number (or rather its square) as being proportional to the force necessary to stop the fluid over the force necessary to compress it by a certain fraction. The larger the Mach number, therefore, the greater the likelihood that pressure variation in the flow will cause significant density changes. At low Mach number the pressure change will normally be insufficient to cause the density to change much, and the flow will behave as if incompressible. An incompressible flow, therefore, may provide as good an approximation to the flow of a compressible gas as to the flow of a less compressible liquid; as far as dynamical behavior is concerned, a flow may be considered incompressible if the Mach number is sufficiently small, independent of how compressible the fluid may be.

12-7 Viscous Compressible Flow

With a finite viscosity and conductivity the equations governing a compressible flow become more complicated. The continuity equation is unchanged, but the momentum equations become (with the usual assumptions about the nature of viscous influence)

$$\rho u \frac{\partial u}{\partial x} + \rho v \frac{\partial u}{\partial y} = -\frac{\partial p}{\partial x} + \mu \left(\frac{\partial^2 u}{\partial x^2} + \frac{\partial^2 u}{\partial y^2} \right)$$
$$+ \frac{1}{3} \mu \frac{\partial}{\partial x} \left(\frac{\partial u}{\partial x} + \frac{\partial v}{\partial y} \right), \quad (12\text{-}36)$$

$$\rho u \frac{\partial v}{\partial x} + \rho v \frac{\partial v}{\partial y} = -\frac{\partial p}{\partial y} + \mu \left(\frac{\partial^2 v}{\partial x^2} + \frac{\partial^2 v}{\partial y^2} \right)$$
$$+ \frac{1}{3} \mu \frac{\partial}{\partial y} \left(\frac{\partial u}{\partial x} + \frac{\partial v}{\partial y} \right). \quad (12\text{-}37)$$

The energy equation is also needed. This may be expressed

$$\rho u \frac{\partial i}{\partial x} + \rho v \frac{\partial i}{\partial y} - u \frac{\partial p}{\partial x} - v \frac{\partial p}{\partial y}$$

$$= -k \left(\frac{\partial^2 T}{\partial x^2} + \frac{\partial^2 T}{\partial y^2} \right) + \phi, \quad (12\text{-}38)$$

where i = enthalpy,
k = thermal conductivity,
T = temperature,
ϕ = dissipation.

The expression for ϕ has the form of viscosity times a complicated collection of velocity derivatives; for our purposes we may denote it as

$$\phi = \mu \left(\frac{\partial u}{\partial y} \right)^2 + \text{similar terms.} \quad (12\text{-}39)$$

In these equations μ and k are assumed constant. The equations will be considered in their application to flow about an insulated cylinder.

The simple equation of state used for the ideal flow is no longer valid, since entropy will not be constant. We may, however, write a similar sort of equation, assuming absolute pressure and temperature to be the independent thermodynamic variables:

$$\frac{d\rho}{\rho} = \delta \frac{dp}{p} - \epsilon \frac{dT}{T}. \quad (12\text{-}40)$$

The parameters δ and ϵ bear some likeness to γ, being expressible as

$$\delta = \frac{p}{\rho} \left(\frac{\partial \rho}{\partial p} \right)_T, \quad (12\text{-}41)$$

$$\epsilon = -\frac{T}{\rho} \left(\frac{\partial \rho}{\partial T} \right)_p. \quad (12\text{-}42)$$

They may be identified, respectively, as the coefficient of compressibility times absolute pressure and the coefficient of thermal expansion times absolute temperature. A thermodynamic equation is also needed for enthalpy. Introducing an additional coefficient c_p, the specific heat at constant pressure, we may express the enthalpy as

$$di = c_p \, dT + (1 - \epsilon) \frac{dp}{\rho} . \qquad (12\text{-}43)$$

At the expense of complicating the equations, one of the three parameters δ, ϵ, and c_p could be eliminated in favor of γ, since

$$\frac{1}{\gamma} = \delta - \frac{\epsilon^2}{c_p} \frac{p}{\rho T} . \qquad (12\text{-}44)$$

The dimensionless variables of Eqs. (12-23) to (12-28) may again be used. The new substantial variables, temperature and enthalpy, may be made dimensionless by adding $c_{p\infty}$ to the previous list of natural units (ρ_∞, V, and D), giving

$$T' = \frac{T - T_\infty}{V^2/c_{p\infty}} , \qquad (12\text{-}45)$$

$$i' = \frac{i - i_\infty}{V^2} . \qquad (12\text{-}46)$$

With these variables substituted, the equations become (omitting the continuity equation, which is unchanged, and the second momentum equation)

$$\rho' u' \frac{\partial u'}{\partial x'} + \rho' v' \frac{\partial u'}{\partial y'} = -\frac{\partial p'}{\partial x'}$$

$$+ \frac{\mu}{\rho_\infty V D} \left[\frac{\partial^2 u'}{\partial x'^2} + \frac{\partial^2 u'}{\partial y'^2} + \frac{1}{3} \frac{\partial}{\partial x'} \left(\frac{\partial u'}{\partial x'} + \frac{\partial v'}{\partial y'} \right) \right],$$
$$(12\text{-}47)$$

$$\rho' u' \frac{\partial i'}{\partial x'} + \rho' v' \frac{\partial i'}{\partial y'} - \left(u' \frac{\partial p'}{\partial x'} + v' \frac{\partial p'}{\partial y'} \right)$$

$$= -\frac{k}{\rho_\infty c_{p\infty} V D} \left(\frac{\partial^2 T'}{\partial x'^2} + \frac{\partial^2 T'}{\partial y'^2} \right)$$

$$+ \frac{\mu}{\rho_\infty V D} \left[\left(\frac{\partial u'}{\partial y'} \right)^2 + \text{similar terms} \right], \quad (12\text{-}48)$$

$$\frac{d\rho'}{\rho'} = \delta \frac{dp'}{p' + p_\infty/\rho_\infty V^2} + \epsilon \frac{dT'}{T' + c_{p\infty} T_\infty/V^2}, \quad (12\text{-}49)$$

$$di' = \frac{c_p}{c_{p\infty}} dT' + (1 - \epsilon) \frac{dp'}{\rho'}. \quad (12\text{-}50)$$

In addition we may rewrite Eq. (12-44) as

$$\frac{1}{\gamma} = \delta - \epsilon^2 \frac{c_{p\infty}}{c_p} \frac{p'}{\rho' T'}. \quad (12\text{-}51)$$

The boundary conditions all come out in terms of pure numbers. At infinity u' and ρ' are unity and p', T', i', and v' are zero. At the cylinder u', v', and the normal derivative of T' are zero.

Looking first at the thermodynamic relations [Eqs. (12-49) and (12-50)], we see that five parameters are involved: $p_\infty/\rho_\infty V^2$, $c_{p\infty} T_\infty/V^2$, $c_p/c_{p\infty}$, δ, and ϵ. The first of these, as we have already seen, may be expressed in terms of Mach number and γ_∞:

$$\frac{\rho_\infty V^2}{p_\infty} = \gamma_\infty \left(\frac{V}{a_\infty} \right)^2. \quad (12\text{-}52)$$

The second may be similarly disposed of, though δ and ϵ also come into the picture; if Eq. (12-44) is evaluated at infinity and combined with Eq. (12-52), it yields

$$\frac{V^2}{c_{p\infty} T_\infty} = \frac{\gamma_\infty \delta_\infty - 1}{\epsilon_\infty^2} \left(\frac{V}{a_\infty} \right)^2. \quad (12\text{-}53)$$

Finally, $c_p/c_{p\infty}$ may be eliminated in favor of γ, δ, and ϵ, with Eq. (12-51):

$$\frac{c_{p\infty}}{c_p} = \frac{\rho'T'}{\epsilon^2 p'}\left(\delta - \frac{1}{\gamma}\right). \tag{12-54}$$

The five parameters may thus be accounted for by the Mach number and the three exponents γ, δ, and ϵ.

For a perfect gas the restrictions imposed are no more severe than in the ideal flow. Both δ and ϵ have a value of unity for all perfect gases so that only γ is left to be reckoned with. The restriction on γ is that it must be the same function of p' and T'. This restriction will be met if γ is the same function of p/p_∞ and T/T_∞, since the relation between the former and the latter variables involves no new parameter:

$$p' = \frac{p_\infty}{\rho_\infty V^2}\left(\frac{p}{p_\infty} - 1\right), \tag{12-55}$$

$$T' = \frac{c_{p\infty}T_\infty}{V^2}\left(\frac{T}{T_\infty} - 1\right). \tag{12-56}$$

For a more general fluid the parameters δ and ϵ will be subject to restrictions similar to those imposed on γ. The restrictions on δ and ϵ may, if desired, be stated in terms of the p-ρ-T relation: δ and ϵ will be the same functions of p' and T' (or p/p_∞ and T/T_∞) if ρ' is the same function of p' and T' (or p/p_∞ and T/T_∞). Specifically, if

$$\rho' = f(p',T'), \tag{12-57}$$

then

$$\delta = \frac{p'}{f}\frac{\partial f}{\partial p'} = f_1(p',T'), \tag{12-58}$$

$$\epsilon = -\frac{T'}{f}\frac{\partial f}{\partial T'} = f_2(p',T'). \tag{12-59}$$

The requirement indicated by Eq. (12-57) would be met by fluids obeying a law of corresponding states if p_∞ and T_∞ were the same fraction of the critical pressure and temperature.

Even if the fluid has the right thermodynamic characteristics and the flow the right Mach number, there are still two more parameters to be respected. These appear in the differential equations [Eqs. (12-47) and (12-48)]. One is the Reynolds number $\rho_\infty VD/\mu$ and the other the Peclet number $\rho_\infty c_{p\infty} VD/k$. Reynolds number has already been discussed. Peclet number is essentially a heat-transfer number and will be discussed later; for a perfect gas it presents no particular problem, since it is a function of Reynolds number and γ.

The flow would have involved several more dimensionless parameters if μ and k had not been assumed constant. If viscosity and conductivity were functions of temperature alone (often a good assumption), their variation could be described by the relations

$$\frac{d\mu}{\mu} = n_1 \frac{dT}{T}, \tag{12-60}$$

$$\frac{dk}{k} = n_2 \frac{dT}{T}. \tag{12-61}$$

Similitude would then require n_1 and n_2 to be the same function of T' or T/T_∞. The presence of a variable μ and k also changes the differential equations slightly, but introduces nothing new for that reason. The variation of μ and k is more often acknowledged—if at all—by assuming them to be constant at some value different from the free-stream value. They might be evaluated, for example, at a temperature approximating the cylinder surface temperature, or perhaps a temperature (usually called the film temperature) halfway between the surface and free-stream temperatures.

A competent dimensional analyst with a good understanding of the flow might well have reached the same, or equivalent, conclusions about the dimensionless parameters of a compressible flow. When the fluid properties are variable, however, it is often difficult to decide how their variability may be characterized without inspecting the equations.

12-8 Knudsen Number

If a flow is sufficiently rarefied, a dimensionless ratio called the Knudsen number is likely to come into prominence. Knudsen number is normally defined as the ratio between the mean free path of the molecules and a characteristic length. When the mean free path is very small compared with other lengths involved, as is the case with ordinary densities and sizes, Knudsen number doesn't enter; but when the mean free path becomes sufficiently large, the equations we have used to describe the flow are no longer entirely appropriate.

The first influence of rarefaction shows up at the boundary; the velocity at a wall cannot be assumed to be zero, as at normal densities. If the mean free path is not too large, the new boundary condition can be written

$$u = l \frac{\partial u}{\partial y}, \qquad (12\text{-}62)$$

where (in this equation) u is velocity parallel to the wall, y the coordinate normal to the wall, and l the mean free path. Writing this equation in dimensionless form gives

$$u' = \frac{l}{D} \frac{\partial u'}{\partial y'}, \qquad (12\text{-}63)$$

revealing at once how Knudsen number (l/D) would get into the picture.

The perfect gas again finds itself in a position of favor, for Knudsen number is not for it a new parameter. It can be shown to be proportional to Mach number over

Reynolds number. For a perfect gas, a situation that appears to involve Reynolds, Mach, and Knudsen numbers could be treated in terms of any two of these three parameters.

12-9 The Dependent Variables of Heat Transfer

So far the dimensionless numbers considered have been those involved in the dynamical behavior of a fluid. Also of interest is its thermal behavior, that is, its ability to carry heat to or from a body. This behavior is usually expressed in terms of a heat-transfer coefficient h, which is the ratio of heat flow per unit of surface to a characteristic temperature difference. The temperature difference that would probably be used to define the heat-transfer coefficient for the cylinder considered previously would be the difference between the actual temperature of the cylinder surface and the temperature it would assume if there were no heat transfer.

From its definition one would expect the heat-transfer coefficient to depend not only on the free-stream properties of the flow but also on the temperature difference; unless the fluid properties are not influenced by temperature change, an increase or decrease in surface temperature would alter the flow. Since this complication obscures the main issue, we shall consider that the heat-transfer coefficient is defined for vanishingly small temperature differences. In practice such a heat-transfer coefficient is a reasonable approximation for finite temperature differences, if not too large (how large being primarily a function of how sensitive the fluid properties are to temperature).

Two dimensionless heat-transfer coefficients are in common use: the Stanton number $h/\rho c_p V$ and the Nusselt number hD/k. If ρ, c_p, and k are variables in the flow, there may be a question of what values to use in writing these numbers; as indicated in the last section, the usual selection (for example, free-stream values) may not always be appropriate if the property variation is not accounted for in other numbers.

The Stanton number and the Nusselt number can both be interpreted as ratios of thermal-energy transfers. These interpretations can be seen more readily if the two numbers are rewritten as follows:

$$\frac{h}{\rho c_p V} = \frac{h \, \Delta T}{(\rho c_p \, \Delta T) V}, \tag{12-64}$$

$$\frac{hD}{k} = \frac{h \, \Delta T}{k \, \Delta T / D}. \tag{12-65}$$

The numerators of these expressions (in which ΔT is a characteristic temperature difference) are proportional to the heat transferred to the fluid (per unit area of surface). The denominators of these expressions are measures of convective and conductive heat transport, respectively: the denominator of the Stanton number expression is proportional to the rate at which thermal energy is borne along by the flow; the denominator of the Nusselt number expression is proportional to the rate at which thermal energy is transferred through the flow by molecular motion.

These interpretations permit immediate prediction of the nature of heat transfer in two limiting cases. If the heat transfer depended predominantly on the convective action, the Stanton number would tend to become constant. This limit is probably not realistic, however, since the transfer of heat from the surface to the fluid will always involve conduction. The other extreme, where heat transfer is almost exclusively by conduction with convection playing no significant role, would result in constant Nusselt number.

The Stanton number and the Nusselt number each has its advantages. The Stanton number has the advantage of relating the heat transfer to what is likely to be the more important agency in a usual flow—although it may be foolish to single out any one sort of flow as usual; it is also closer kin of the dimensionless numbers of fluid dynamics (where, for example, pressure and shear stress are commonly referred to ρV^2, a measure of convective momentum transport, rather than $\mu V/D$, a measure of molecular momentum transport). Nusselt number, however, has the advantage that it may serve to describe heat transfer when V is zero. It is also—perhaps for this reason—the more widely used.

12-10 Peclet Number

Thermal similitude in a flow can be secured if, in addition to the numbers involved in dynamic similitude, the Peclet number $\rho c_p VD/k$ is made the same. This conclusion may be drawn from the equations of Sec. 12-7, which are based on the assumption that heat transfer to the flow was absent; however, as explained in the last section, a heat-transfer coefficient having practical significance may be defined for such a flow. In an incompressible flow the Peclet number will be involved if temperature or heat transfer is of interest; in a flow where the drag coefficient or other dimensionless dynamic parameter is dependent on Reynolds number alone, the Nusselt number or other dimensionless thermal parameter would depend on both Reynolds number and Peclet number. In a compressible flow, dynamic and thermal similitude are inseparably bound, so that Peclet number (or a substitute) will always be involved, unless conduction can be neglected.

The Peclet number can be interpreted as a sort of thermal Reynolds number, provided that a new interpretation is given to Reynolds number. The two numbers can be expressed as

$$\frac{\rho V D}{\mu} = \frac{(\rho V) V}{\mu V / D} \,, \qquad (12\text{-}66)$$

$$\frac{\rho c_p V D}{k} = \frac{(\rho c_p \, \Delta T) V}{k \, \Delta T / D} \,. \qquad (12\text{-}67)$$

The numerator of the rewritten Reynolds number is proportional to the rate at which momentum is transported by fluid motion, and the denominator is proportional to the rate at which momentum is transported by molecular motion. The numerator of the rewritten Peclet number [which is the denominator of Eq. (12-64)] is proportional to the rate at which thermal energy is transported by fluid motion, and the denominator [which is the denominator of Eq. (12-65)] is proportional to the rate at which thermal energy is transported by molecular motion. The Peclet number, therefore, bears the same relationship to thermal energy that Reynolds number does to momentum.

A somewhat more specific interpretation of these numbers is available if we consider their significance in laminar and turbulent flows. In laminar flow Reynolds number or Peclet number can be interpreted as an inverse measure of the tendency of the momentum or thermal energy (respectively) to diffuse, that is, to spread laterally rather than be borne along by the fluid. In a turbulent flow the Reynolds number or Peclet number can be regarded as proportional to the ratio of turbulent transport of momentum or thermal energy (respectively) to molecular transport.

12-11 Prandtl Number

The Prandtl number is commonly used as a replacement for Peclet number. It can be formed as the ratio of Peclet number to Reynolds number:

$$\frac{c_p \mu}{k} = \frac{\rho c_p VD/k}{\rho VD/\mu}.$$
(12-68)

Any flow involving Reynolds number and Peclet number can then alternatively be handled with Reynolds number and Prandtl number (or for that matter with Peclet and Prandtl numbers). The attractive feature of Prandtl number, besides involving three rather than five variables, is that (like the adiabatic exponent γ that shows up in flow similitude) it is merely a fluid property. Furthermore, for a perfect gas it is a function of γ and therefore does not represent an additional restriction on similitude.

The Prandtl number can best be interpreted in terms of diffusive tendencies in laminar motion. Since the Peclet number is an inverse measure of the tendency for thermal energy to diffuse and the Reynolds number an inverse measure of the tendency for momentum to diffuse, their ratio, the Prandtl number, is a measure of the tendency of momentum to diffuse as compared with thermal energy (in a laminar flow). Consistent with this interpretation, the Prandtl number is often written as the ratio ν/α, where $\alpha = k/\rho c_p$ is the thermal diffusivity and $\nu = \mu/\rho$ is the kinematic viscosity, which can be thought of as the momentum diffusivity.

While Prandtl number is a fine substitute for Peclet number in any flow which involves Reynolds number, it is not appropriate in a flow that does not. In an unaccelerated laminar flow or a highly turbulent flow, for example, Reynolds number is not present as a similitude parameter; therefore, Nusselt number (or Stanton number) is a function of Peclet number alone.

12-12   Graetz Number

The Graetz number is another dimensionless number associated with convective heat transfer. It originated in the study of laminar heat transfer in a pipe and was expressed as mc_p/kL, where m is mass flow rate and L the pipe length. For a round pipe it can be rewritten as

$$\frac{mc_p}{kL} = \frac{\pi}{4}\frac{D^2\rho V c_p}{kL} = \frac{\pi}{4}\frac{\rho c_p V D}{k}\cdot\frac{D}{L}.\qquad(12\text{-}69)$$

In other words, it is simply a Peclet number multiplied by $\pi/4$ times the diameter-length ratio. Since the flow giving rise to it is an unaccelerated laminar flow, the emergence of Peclet number is hardly a surprise after the closing remarks of the last section.

12-13   Free Convection

Gravity influences a flow in two fairly distinct ways. As already considered, it influences the form of the free surface. It may also give rise to a circulation of fluid termed free, or natural, convection. The former influence is normally described in terms of a Froude number, the latter influence in terms of Grashof number. The Grashof number is usually written $\rho^2 g\beta\,\Delta T D^3/\mu^2$, where β is the coefficient of thermal expansion of the fluid and ΔT is a characteristic temperature difference. (The other symbols are as previously defined.)

Free convection is present in just about any flow in which density variation and gravity are present. It is usually important, however, only in situations where the flow velocities are low and heat transfer is present to give rise to sufficient density variation.

How Grashof number gets into the picture is most easily demonstrated by considering a flow that is nearly incompressible, but not quite. Specifically, density change is ignored except for its influence on a single term in the vertical momentum equation, a term which is identified as a buoyant term. If the vertical momentum equation for an incompressible flow [Eq. (9-40)] is written with the pressure referred to the pressure at infinity, it reads

$$\rho u \frac{\partial v}{\partial x} + \rho v \frac{\partial v}{\partial y} = -\frac{\partial(p - p_\infty)}{\partial y}$$

$$+ (\rho_\infty - \rho)g + \mu \left(\frac{\partial^2 v}{\partial x^2} + \frac{\partial^2 v}{\partial y^2} \right), \quad (12\text{-}70)$$

in which use is made of the fact that

$$\frac{\partial p_\infty}{\partial y} = -\rho_\infty g. \quad (12\text{-}71)$$

The second term on the right would drop out in a truly incompressible flow; however, now the density at the point described is presumed to be a small but significant amount different from the ambient density. This term is usually called the buoyant-force term, since it is equal to the buoyant force that would be experienced by a unit volume of the fluid at the point described if it were immersed in the ambient fluid. For the sake of its evaluation it is common to assume that the ambient density is related to the local density through a linear function of temperature,

$$\rho_\infty = \rho[1 - \beta(T_\infty - T)], \quad (12\text{-}72)$$

which implies that the density change is not great and that the effect of pressure on density can be neglected compared to the effect of temperature. The buoyant term then becomes

$$(\rho_\infty - \rho)g = \rho g \beta (T - T_\infty). \qquad (12\text{-}73)$$

Once this term is secured, the density ρ is considered uniform throughout.

Analogous to Reynolds number or to Froude number (squared), we can now invent a dimensionless number (unnamed) proportional to the ratio of inertia to buoyant force:

$$\frac{\rho V^2/D}{\rho g \beta \, \Delta T} = \frac{V^2}{g \beta \, \Delta T D}. \qquad (12\text{-}74)$$

(In terms of parameters previously encountered, this number may be recognized as the square of the Froude number over $\beta \, \Delta T$. The latter parameter is akin to $\epsilon = \beta T$, the compressible-flow parameter of Sec. 12-7. A more significant interpretation is that it is the square of a modified Froude number based on the buoyant force per unit mass, $g \beta \, \Delta T$, rather than the gravitational force per unit mass, g.) In a nearly incompressible flow in which free convection cannot be ignored, therefore, we could argue that the heat transfer could be expressed as

$$\frac{hD}{k} = f\left(\frac{\rho V D}{\mu}, \frac{c_p \mu}{k}, \frac{V^2}{g \beta \, \Delta T D}\right). \qquad (12\text{-}75)$$

This relationship can be rewritten in a better form if velocity is eliminated from one of the terms in which it appears. Combining Reynolds number with the new number in the following manner gives a substitute that does not contain velocity:

$$\left(\frac{\rho V D}{\mu}\right)^2 \left(\frac{g \beta \, \Delta T D}{V^2}\right) = \frac{\rho^2 g \beta \, \Delta T D^3}{\mu^2}. \qquad (12\text{-}76)$$

We may therefore write

$$\frac{hD}{k} = f\left(\frac{\rho V D}{\mu}, \frac{c_p\mu}{k}, \frac{\rho^2 g\beta\,\Delta T D^3}{\mu^2}\right), \qquad (12\text{-}77)$$

in which the added number is now recognized as the Grashof number. (It is seen to have the complicated equivalent of Reynolds number squared times $\beta\,\Delta T$ over Froude number squared, or alternatively the square of the ratio of Reynolds number to modified Froude number.)

The reason for preferring Eq. (12-77) to Eq. (12-75) is that an important instance of free convection (in fact, the most important) is when the free-stream velocity V is zero. In this case one (but only one) of the dimensionless ratios should drop out, so that for the sake of this limit the equation is appropriately written with V in only one term. For wholly free convection Eq. (12-77) would then indicate that

$$\frac{hD}{k} = f\left(\frac{\rho^2 g\beta\,\Delta T D^3}{\mu^2}, \frac{c_p\mu}{k}\right). \qquad (12\text{-}78)$$

An interpretation of the Grashof number in terms of forces is available from the foregoing. From Eq. (12-76) we see that it is proportional to the ratio of inertia force times buoyant force over viscous force squared. A further interpretation is possible if an assumption is made. If it is assumed that the pressure term $\partial(p - p_\infty)/\partial y$ in the differential equation is unimportant (as it is in most instances of pure free convection), then we may argue that a balance will obtain between the inertia, viscous, and buoyant forces on a particle, or

$$F_b = F_i + F_v. \qquad (12\text{-}79)$$

With this assumption, the forces to which Grashof number is proportional can be rewritten as follows:

$$\frac{F_i F_b}{F_v{}^2} = \left(\frac{F_i}{F_v}\right)^2 + \frac{F_i}{F_v} = \left(\frac{F_i}{F_v} + \frac{1}{2}\right)^2 - \frac{1}{4}. \quad (12\text{-}80)$$

We see in this some basis for the common practice of regarding Grashof number as a special sort of Reynolds number.

The role of Grashof and Prandtl numbers in the limiting types of free convection can be readily deduced. Of most practical interest is the nature of the viscous limit. In the absence of free convection we have already decided that for flow in which inertia plays no part the only dimensionless parameter required for similitude is the Peclet number. In free convection, however, another number should appear because of the presence of buoyant forces. That number may be formed as a ratio of terms proportional to the buoyant and viscous forces:

$$\frac{\rho g \beta \, \Delta T}{\mu V / D^2} = \frac{\rho g \beta \, \Delta T D^2}{\mu V}. \qquad (12\text{-}81)$$

We therefore conclude that in a flow involving free convection, but in which inertia forces are small, a relation of the following sort should hold true:

$$\frac{hD}{k} = f\left(\frac{\rho g \beta \, \Delta T D^2}{\mu V}, \frac{\rho c_p V D}{k}\right). \qquad (12\text{-}82)$$

Rewriting this relation in a form that leaves velocity in only one term, we get

$$\frac{hD}{k} = f\left(\frac{\rho^2 c_p g \beta \, \Delta T D^3}{\mu k}, \frac{\rho c_p V D}{k}\right). \qquad (12\text{-}83)$$

With V zero the first of these terms survives; it may be identified as the product of Grashof and Prandtl numbers:

$$\frac{\rho^2 c_p g \beta \, \Delta T D^3}{\mu k} = \frac{\rho^2 g \beta \, \Delta T D^3}{\mu^2} \cdot \frac{c_p \mu}{k}. \qquad (12\text{-}84)$$

This number, which is sometimes called the modified Grashof number, finds frequent use in free-convection correlations.

Dependence of Nusselt number on the product of Grashof and Prandtl number represents a limit only from the standpoint of fluid flow. If the convective influences become unimportant, not only in the momentum transport, but also in the heat transport, then the Peclet number in Eq. (12-82) must lose influence, leaving Nusselt number a constant (when V is zero). This limit, encountered at very low values of the Grashof-Prandtl product, corresponds to conduction into a fluid whose motion is insufficient to have any influence.

The limiting case at the other end of the scale, where viscous forces become unimportant, may be analyzed in similar fashion. Here we would expect the number defined [in Eq. (12-74)] as proportional to the ratio of inertia to buoyant forces to enter, along with Peclet number:

$$\frac{hD}{k} = f\left(\frac{V^2}{g\beta \, \Delta TD}, \frac{\rho c_p VD}{k}\right). \qquad (12\text{-}85)$$

This we may write with V in only one term as

$$\frac{hD}{k} = f\left(\frac{\rho^2 c_p{}^2 g\beta \, \Delta TD^3}{k^2}, \frac{\rho c_p VD}{k}\right). \qquad (12\text{-}86)$$

The new number in this case can be identified as another combination of Grashof number and Prandtl number (the combination needed to eliminate μ):

$$\frac{\rho^2 c_p{}^2 g\beta \, \Delta TD^3}{k^2} = \frac{\rho^2 g\beta \, \Delta TD^3}{\mu^2}\left(\frac{c_p \mu}{k}\right)^2. \qquad (12\text{-}87)$$

By this argument the Nusselt number for highly turbulent free convection should depend on just the product of Grashof number and Prandtl number squared.

We may again look beyond the fluid-flow limit to the limit where heat flow as well does not depend on molecular transport. For the heat transfer to be independent of conductivity would require the Nusselt number to be proportional to Prandtl number, so that k will cancel. Combining this requirement with the requirement for zero viscous influences gives

$$\frac{hD}{k} \sim \left(\frac{\rho^2 g\beta \,\Delta T D^3}{\mu^2}\right)^{1/2} \frac{c_p\mu}{k}. \qquad (12\text{-}88)$$

In practice the highest power of Grashof number ordinarily encountered in free convection is $\frac{1}{3}$ rather than $\frac{1}{2}$. As suggested previously, it is to be expected that conductivity will continue to have an influence on heat flow in any real situation. Equation (12-88) might be expected, however, to represent the asymptote approached as Grashof number becomes infinite.

These conclusions about the limiting cases can be reached by another route, namely, dimensional analysis. This approach provides an interesting example of technique. With a little thought it may be concluded that the following characteristic parameters are involved in a pure free convection. The reasons for the involvement of the independent variables are indicated parenthetically.

h	heat-transfer coefficient
ρ	density (inertial influence)
$\rho g\beta$	buoyant force per unit volume per unit temperature difference (buoyant influence)
μ	viscosity (viscous influence)
k	conductivity (influence of heat conduction)
ρc_p	volumetric specific heat (influence of heat storage)
D	length (size influence)
ΔT	temperature difference (primal cause)

The groupings of variables are significant. The inclusion of ρ in $\rho g\beta$ and ρc_p is for the sake of referring these properties to a unit volume rather than a unit mass; otherwise it would be harder to deduce what happens when mass becomes unimportant to the problem; that is, when inertia forces are unimportant. The grouping of β and ρg amounts to arguing that the volume changes are of significance only in their effect on buoyancy. Were β included separately, the dimensionless parameter $\beta \, \Delta T$ could immediately be formed; this parameter is related to expansion influences that are not regarded as significant in the present problem.

If it is assumed that we have collected a proper set of variables, a dimensional analysis reveals a result of the following form:

$$\frac{hD}{k} = f\left[\frac{\rho(\rho g \beta)\,\Delta T D^3}{\mu^2}, \frac{(\rho c_p)\mu}{\rho k}, \frac{(\rho g \beta)D}{(\rho c_p)}\right]. \quad (12\text{-}89)$$

The first two numbers are recognized as Grashof number and Prandtl number. The third is something new, but fortunately we can argue our way out of accepting it. It has the form of a ratio of work done by buoyant forces over thermal energy stored. In the usual free-convection situation, however, the buoyant work is a piddling contribution in the energy balance, so that the associated number can readily be ignored.

The limiting cases are now easy to explore. If inertia forces are unimportant, the two numbers must appear in a combination that eliminates density (where by itself); therefore the Grashof and Prandtl numbers must appear as a product:

$$\frac{hD}{k} = f\left[\frac{\rho(\rho g \beta)\,\Delta T D^3}{\mu^2} \cdot \frac{(\rho c_p)\mu}{\rho k}\right]$$

$$= f\left[\frac{(\rho c_p)(\rho g \beta)\,\Delta T D^3}{\mu k}\right]. \quad (12\text{-}90)$$

If viscous forces are unimportant, viscosity must be

eliminated; this requires Grashof number and Prandtl number squared to appear as a product:

$$\frac{hD}{k} = f\left\{\frac{\rho(\rho g\beta)\,\Delta T D^3}{\mu^2}\left[\frac{(\rho c_p)\mu}{\rho k}\right]^2\right\}$$

$$= f\left[\frac{(\rho c_p)^2(\rho g\beta)\,\Delta T D^3}{\rho k^2}\right]. \qquad (12\text{-}91)$$

The further limits considered may be found by eliminating ρc_p and k appropriately.

13

The Comparison of
Geometrically Dissimilar Systems

13-1 Introduction

The dimensionless relations so far considered have
not contained the physical shape as a variable. Poten-
tially, however, many of these dimensionless relations
include the dimensionless numbers that describe shape,
in addition to the other numbers involved in similitude.
If, for example, the drag coefficient of similarly shaped
cylinders were found to depend only on Reynolds number, one would conclude that for differently shaped
cylinders drag coefficient would depend on Reynolds
number plus one or more shape parameters. For elliptical cylinders, two shape parameters would be involved: the eccentricity and the angle between the
major axis and the flow direction. The latter variable,
an angle of attack, has nothing to do with the shape of
the cylinder but is clearly needed to describe the shape
of the system.

214

The complete description of shape is a straightforward problem, and it is not the aim of this chapter to consider it. The real aim is to consider how one may get by with an incomplete description of shape, or none at all. What may be done in this direction depends partly on what is sought: what is adequate for some answers is not for others. An adequate description of a pin on the head of which the Lord's Prayer is engraved, for example, is quite dependent on whether one is concerned with saving one's modesty or one's soul. But the problem is often more than deciding what aspects of shape seem most pertinent to the situation; the influence of shape is often tied up with the influence of the other numbers involved, and the question of how to characterize shape often becomes a question of how best to form the other dimensionless numbers, in particular, how best to characterize the size.

For the most part the technique of handling shape can be presented only by examples. Some effort is made to wrest generalities from the examples; but since the problem more often involves the vague question of what may be expected to provide the best or the broadest approximation than the precise question of what is correct, the generalities do not take the form of rules, but only of suggestions.

13-2 Selection of a Characteristic Length

How shape affects a dimensionless relation depends in part on what length is used in the numbers that involve length. In a relation for the drag on a circular cylinder of diameter D and span L placed transverse to the flow, for example, how D and L are used in the drag coefficient and the Reynolds number will strongly affect the role of L/D, the shape parameter. If the drag coefficient uses DL (the frontal area) as a reference and the Reynolds number uses D, then L/D will have no influence if sufficiently large. Here the basis for the choice is easy to see. The presence of L in the drag coefficient essentially reduces drag to drag per unit length, which should become independent of L if L/D is large enough; if D is used in the other locations where a length is called for, the correlation will then become independent of L/D at large values of that parameter. With any other choice of reference lengths, the effect of shape (in the form of L/D) would always be present.

Considerations of the nature of the flow usually decide the best characteristic lengths and areas in flow problems. Where drag is largely due to pressure difference, drag coefficient is usually referred to frontal area and Reynolds number to some length transverse to the flow; where drag is largely due to shear stress, drag coefficient is usually referred to a surface area (or more likely a plan area) and Reynolds number to some length along the flow. Drag on an airfoil, for example, is referred to the plan area, and the Reynolds number is based on the chord. Such selections of characteristic lengths and areas seldom completely eliminate shape effects, but they often help; the drag coefficient for an airfoil—expressed in this way—is not a strong function of the thickness-chord ratio if that ratio is small.

But there is no firm rule to guide the selection of the best characteristic length or area. Occasionally pure empiricism provides the answer, though usually theory supplies the clues. Failure to make the best choice will generally mean that shape exerts a larger influence on the relation than necessary, which is not inevitably a disadvantage.

13-3 Distorted Hydraulic Models

Tidal flows in harbors, bays, or estuaries provide another instance where a shape parameter may be rendered unimportant by the proper choice of a characteristic length. In flows such as these where horizontal distances are large compared with depths and where surface disturbances are caused by the shore line or by long-period phenomena such as tides, the flow (assuming that viscous influence can be ignored) is essentially uniform as a function of depth. The important consideration for similitude is the similarity of depth variation, which will entail not only the same bottom profiles but also the same surface profiles. Since the features of surface profiles move relative to the water, the velocities of their movement (the wave velocities) must bear the same relationship to the flow velocities if the surface character is to be the same. The wave velocity for wavelengths long compared with depth is proportional to the square root of the product of depth and the acceleration of gravity; therefore, the flow and wave velocities will be in the same proportion if a Froude number based on depth is the same.

A Froude number involving a flow velocity is not ordinarily an independent variable in the sort of problem considered; however, an independent velocity which is characteristic of the system may be formed. If the period of the tidal phenomenon is T and L is a characteristic horizontal dimension, then L/T provides a proper characteristic velocity to which other velocities will be proportional. Therefore the Froude number required for similitude may be expressed as $L/T\sqrt{Dg}$, in which D is a characteristic depth. If this requirement is accepted as sufficient for similitude, there is no reason why the vertical distances must be scaled the same as the horizontal distances; the shape parameter L/D is not involved as a separate parameter, and therefore distortion of the vertical scale is permissible without destruction of similitude. The Froude number will be the same (assuming no change in g) if the time scale is related to the length scales by the equation

$$\lambda_t = \frac{\lambda_l}{\sqrt{\lambda_d}}, \tag{13-1}$$

where l refers to the horizontal scale and d to the vertical; there is no requirement that λ_d equal λ_l.

The possibility of scaling the horizontal and vertical distances differently is more than an interesting phenomenon: it is a practical necessity in many model problems of this sort. If uniform scaling is used, the depth is likely to become so shallow that viscous effects become important. If depth is scaled down less than width, it may be possible to keep Reynolds number high enough to give no trouble. (The Reynolds number would properly be based on depth, since equivalent diameter—which is discussed in the next section—is proportional to depth for a shallow flow.) The scale factor for Reynolds number will be

$$\lambda_{\mathrm{Re}} = \lambda_v \lambda_d = \frac{\lambda_l}{\lambda_t} \lambda_d = \lambda_d^{3/2} \tag{13-2}$$

if the fluid properties aren't changed. (By distorting the depth the Reynolds number goes up, not only because the depth itself goes up, but also because the velocities go up.)

Weber number, the number involving surface tension, is not affected by such distortion. Presumably the proper length for characterizing the surface-tension effect is the radius of curvature of the surface, which will depend inversely on the second derivative of surface elevation with respect to a horizontal coordinate. This derivative will scale as the depth scale over the square of the width scale. Therefore Weber number will scale as

$$\lambda_{We} = \frac{\lambda_v{}^2\lambda_l{}^2}{\lambda_d} = \left(\frac{\lambda_l}{\lambda_t}\right)^2 \frac{\lambda_l{}^2}{\lambda_d} = \lambda_l{}^2 \qquad (13\text{-}3)$$

for the same density and surface tension. The only cure for surface tension, if it's a problem, would appear to be to increase the horizontal scale or the density (or to decrease the surface tension).

Although in this example similitude is preserved in spite of a shape change (as long as viscous and surface forces are unimportant), more commonly a shape change will destroy similitude and the only hope is that some of the relations may still be valid in spite of the change. In other words, the question is often not whether shape will affect similitude but whether it will affect all the dimensionless relations that are valid under conditions of similitude.

13-4 Equivalent Diameter

Pipe, or channel, flow provides an instance where very simple considerations have suggested a characteristic length that has proved useful in minimizing shape influence when similitude is destroyed. As indicated in Sec. 12-2, the frictional effect in pipe flow may be expressed in two slightly different ways, depending on whether one wishes to talk about pressure drop or wall shear stress. For a smooth circular pipe these expressions have the form

$$\frac{\Delta p D}{\frac{1}{2}\rho V^2 L} = f_1\left(\frac{\rho V D}{\mu}\right), \tag{13-4}$$

$$\frac{\tau_o}{\frac{1}{8}\rho V^2} = f_1\left(\frac{\rho V D}{\mu}\right), \tag{13-5}$$

where the left-hand sides are alternative representations of the friction factor f. If both these expressions are to continue to be valid for a noncircular pipe, there is no freedom of choice of the equivalent diameter to be used in the left-hand side of Eq. (13-4), since it is determined by the relationship between pressure drop and shear stress. In general the pressure drop and the mean shear stress are related by the equation

$$\Delta p A = \tau_o P L, \tag{13-6}$$

where A is flow area and P is perimeter (in channel flow, the wetted perimeter only). Combining this equation with Eqs. (13-4) and (13-5) reveals that

$$D = \frac{4A}{P}. \tag{13-7}$$

An equivalent diameter equal to four times the area over the wetted perimeter is therefore a logical replacement for the diameter appearing in the friction factor.

What equivalent diameter (if any) will give the same function f_1 when used in the Reynolds number is not answered by the same logic; however, the equivalent diameter defined for the sake of the friction factor is an obvious first guess. Its use in this capacity is prevalent and moderately successful. Barring shapes that would give rise to more or less distinct regions of flow, its use is generally well regarded for turbulent flow, though not for laminar flow. It is likely that this judgment is somewhat dependent on the fact that turbulent friction factor is a weaker function of Reynolds number than laminar. In laminar flow the approximation is also more readily and decisively challenged by theory and may be shown in specific cases to come out a poor second.

13-5   Equivalent Description of Size and Shape

The idea of equivalence has general usefulness in the description of size and shape. The equivalent diameter of pipe flow is a rather special example of how equivalence may be arrived at, though it is still a valid example. When it is difficult to decide what aspect of size or shape is significant, it is often helpful to relate a particular aspect of size or shape to a standard system having only the one aspect. The difficulty of defining the size of a noncircular pipe was solved by relating it to a system involving only size: a circular pipe. The relationship that ties the two systems together was arbitrary, though pertinent; namely, that they should have the same ratio of mean shear stress to pressure drop per unit length.

In general the relationship available is more likely to be in terms of performance. For pipe flow, for example, one might have defined an equivalent diameter as the characteristic length that would give the same laminar friction factor as a circular pipe—more difficult to figure, but not impossible. The hope would then be that, with one feature of performance precisely matched, other features, such as turbulent friction, might fall in line as well. One might, as another example, define the aspect ratio of a wing (which is normally defined as the ratio of span to mean chord) as equal to the aspect ratio of a standard elliptical wing giving the same lift-curve slope; and one might hope that such an equivalent aspect ratio might prove a more effective description of shape than an aspect ratio arbitrarily defined in terms of geometry.

A good example of this approach is the description of roughness. In turbulent flow surface roughness is likely to have a large influence on wall shear stress; it is also influential in such phenomena as boundary-layer transition and separation. The simplest description of roughness would be in terms of a length characteristic of the roughness. (Roughness so described would normally enter the equations as a shape parameter called the relative roughness formed as the ratio of the roughness to a length characteristic of the system.) In view of the irregular nature of roughness, it is not immediately clear what length to use in characterizing it. The approach now commonly used in pipe flow is to define the roughness in terms of the diameter of sand particles that will give the same effect at high Reynolds number, if such particles are used to create an artificially roughened surface. The single length parameter established in this manner provides an incomplete characterization of roughness but at least accounts for the major influence; and it has the advantage, which would not be expected of any direct measurement of roughness, of at least being a precise measure at the limit of full turbulence.

Although the hope in establishing an equivalence may often be that the size or shape so defined will tell the whole story, failure of this hope does not necessarily render the equivalence useless. The validity of the sand grain for characterizing the size of roughness does not hang on the demonstration that all pipes having the same equivalent roughness behave the same. If they don't (as they don't), it simply means that size alone is inadequate to describe roughness; it does not mean that the measure of size is inappropriate.

13-6   Replacement of the Shape Parameter

The use of an equivalent size or shape parameter, as described in the last section, is often an unnecessary artifice. Equivalent roughness is an example. It was not really essential to coat the interior of pipes with sand just for the sake of establishing a measure of roughness; it would have been quite as proper to define roughness in terms of the friction factor f^* experienced at high Reynolds number. The friction factor f could then be expressible as a function of Reynolds number and f^*. There would remain the problem of relating the physical surface character to f^*, which would replace the present problem of relating it to the equivalent sand-grain roughness. Although defining the sand-grain roughness results in a somewhat better framework for estimations of actual roughness, it is worth recognizing that the framework is a luxury and not a necessity.

The best way of characterizing shape in terms of performance is usually found by looking at some special feature of performance. Limiting-case performance provided the clue for relative roughness. Optimum-point performance may also provide the needed relation. Such a performance point is of particular interest if it corresponds to the design point of the system, as it might for a machine, for then it may be possible to characterize the shape in terms of design-point parameters.

The influence of shape on a system for which there is an optimum point can be expressed in fairly general terms. Its influence is made clearer if the performance is expressed in terms of the optimum-point performance. How this can be accomplished may be demonstrated for a simple system having the characteristics represented by an equation of the sort

$$A = f_1(B, S), \tag{13-8}$$

where A as a function of B exhibits a maximum at the optimum point and where S is a shape parameter. (The parameter A might be an efficiency and B a dimensionless speed or flow rate, or the like.) If we now let

$$\frac{\partial A}{\partial B} = f_2(B, S) \tag{13-9}$$

and denote optimum-point parameters by asterisked variables, then

$$f_2(B^*, S) = 0 \tag{13-10}$$

defines the optimum point. From this equation it follows that

$$B^* = f_3(S) \tag{13-11}$$

and similarly [from Eq. (13-8)] that

$$A^* = f_1(B^*, S) = f_4(S). \tag{13-12}$$

It is also evident that

$$\frac{A}{A^*} = f_5\left(\frac{B}{B^*}, S\right). \tag{13-13}$$

In other words, the values of A and B at the optimum point and the nature of the curve of A as a fraction of its optimum-point value versus B as a fraction of its optimum-point value are all functions only of shape.

If, as assumed, shape may be represented by a single parameter, it is evident that these last three equations provide a basis for its characterization in terms of a performance parameter. In particular Eq. (13-11) indicates that

$$S = f_6(B^*), \tag{13-14}$$

so that B^*, the optimum-point value of the independent

performance variable, may serve to characterize shape. Equations (13-12) and (13-13) may then take the form

$$\frac{A}{A^*} = f_7\left(\frac{B}{B^*}, B^*\right), \qquad (13\text{-}15)$$

$$A^* = f_8(B^*). \qquad (13\text{-}16)$$

Other independent parameters that might also be expressible as a function of the performance variable B and the single shape parameter S would fit into this scheme as well. The shape of their curves as a function of B and their optimum-point values would depend on B^* alone. Of course, A^* or any other optimum-point value responsive to shape might be used in place of B^* for the sake of characterizing shape. An example of this sort of shape characterization is given in the next section.

If more than a single parameter is necessary to describe shape, the same sort of substitution is possible, though correspondingly more performance variables will be needed to characterize the shape. If, for example,

$$A = f_1(B, S_1, S_2), \qquad (13\text{-}17)$$

where S_1 and S_2 are both shape parameters, the role of shape is much as before; that is,

$$\frac{A}{A^*} = f_2\left(\frac{B}{B^*}, S_1, S_2\right), \qquad (13\text{-}18)$$

$$A^* = f_3(S_1, S_2), \qquad (13\text{-}19)$$
$$B^* = f_4(S_1, S_2). \qquad (13\text{-}20)$$

The last two equations do not as before reveal a direct relation between A^* and B^*; they do, however, indicate that

$$S_1 = f_5(A^*, B^*), \qquad (13\text{-}21)$$
$$S_2 = f_6(A^*, B^*). \qquad (13\text{-}22)$$

Therefore Eq. (13-18) could take the form

$$\frac{A}{A^*} = f\left(\frac{B}{B^*}, A^*, B^*\right). \qquad (13\text{-}23)$$

Thus A^* as well as B^* enters as an independent parameter. Other optimum-point parameters (and curve shapes) would now be a function of A^* and B^* (or any other two optimum-point parameters).

13-7   Selection of the Characterizing Parameter

The characterization of shape by a performance parameter is likely to involve more than merely picking a handy performance parameter and going ahead. To characterize shape properly, the parameter must naturally be continuously responsive to shape changes. It is also a decided advantage in some applications if the parameter does not include length as a factor, for the characterization of length may be a problem itself.

A good example of the considerations involved is available from a study of the performance of hydrodynamic pumps. As a preliminary it will be necessary to establish the form of the dimensionless relations involved. The relations are most easily arrived at by dimensional analysis, although this approach involves the avoidance of an interesting pitfall.

The first question of performance is the pressure rise developed as a function of the flow rate and the other parameters involved. If, for simplicity, it is assumed that the flow is incompressible and that Reynolds number is high enough so that viscosity has no direct influence on performance, the pressure rise developed by the pump will depend on the volume flow rate Q, the rotative speed N, the fluid density ρ, and the size. Characterizing the size by the impeller diameter D, we may write

$$\Delta p = f(Q, N, \rho, D). \qquad (13\text{-}24)$$

A dimensional analysis reduces this equation to the dimensionless form

$$\frac{\Delta p}{\rho N^2 D^2} = f\left(\frac{Q}{ND^3}\right). \qquad (13\text{-}25)$$

Since in normal pump parlance head (H), as defined by

$$\Delta p = \rho g H, \qquad (13\text{-}26)$$

is generally spoken of rather than pressure rise, we may write Eq. (13-25) in more conventional form as

$$\frac{gH}{N^2 D^2} = f\left(\frac{Q}{ND^3}\right). \qquad (13\text{-}27)$$

An interesting lesson in dimensional analysis is available from a study of Eq. (13-27). The equation suggests that we might alternatively have started with the presumption that H is a function of Q, N, g, and D, rather than Δp a function of Q, N, ρ, and D. Had we done so, however, we would have come up with an additional dimensionless number H/D, making similitude appear more difficult. What happens in such an approach is that we are asking for more similitude than we want: there is no desire for the ratio between the height to which the fluid may rise and the pump size to conform to a rule of similarity. Of course after-thought will work as well as forethought: if one inadvertently comes up with the three terms, one can then argue that they must combine in such a fashion that head developed is inversely proportional to g, other things being equal. Such an argument would immediately drop out H/D as a legitimate term.

From Eq. (13-27) we see that similitude may be ensured by equality of the number Q/ND^3 (provided, of course, that shape is preserved). The number Q/ND^3, a dimensionless flow rate, may be interpreted as a ratio of a term proportional to the fluid velocities to a term proportional to the impeller velocity:

$$\frac{Q}{ND^3} = \frac{Q/D^2}{ND}. \qquad (13\text{-}28)$$

The parameter Q/ND^3 might of course also serve as an independent variable in describing other aspects of performance dimensionlessly. The efficiency, for example, would follow a relation of the same sort:

$$\eta = f\left(\frac{Q}{ND^3}\right). \qquad (13\text{-}29)$$

(To fit properly into such a relation, the efficiency would have to be defined in terms of power requirements of the fluid only, that is, as a ratio of the power ideally required by the fluid to the power actually required.) A power number, which might be formed as $P/\rho N^3 D^5$, in which P is power required by the fluid, would also be expressible as a function of Q/ND^3. (This number would, in fact, be just gH/N^2D^2 times Q/ND^3 over η.)

We have now reached the point where we may consider the role of shape in pump performance. If, as an example, we consider a family of centrifugal pumps that are nonsimilar, but whose geometric differences can be characterized by the single shape parameter, the ratio of the width of the impeller passage at the periphery to the impeller diameter (b/D), then Eqs. (13-27) and (13-29) become

$$\frac{gH}{N^2D^2} = f_1\left(\frac{Q}{ND^3}, \frac{b}{D}\right), \qquad (13\text{-}30)$$

$$\eta = f_2\left(\frac{Q}{ND^3}, \frac{b}{D}\right). \qquad (13\text{-}31)$$

The second of these equations is of the type considered

in the last section. It is therefore possible to characterize the shape by the optimum-point value of Q/ND^3, which would be the value of Q/ND^3 giving peak efficiency. The shape of the curves of head vs. flow and efficiency vs. flow, as well as the optimum-point values of η and gH/N^2D^2, would then be functions of the optimum-point value of Q/ND^3 alone.

The parameter Q/ND^3 is, however, not the best-suited for this use. Although it has the advantage of being a strong and steady function of shape, its value is very sensitive to the choice of D. If there is difficulty in defining an effective value of b/D, there is quite likely to be difficulty in defining an effective value of D. The other parameters appearing in the equations, η and gH/N^2D^2, might alternatively be used to characterize shape: however, neither is any better, nor even as good. The peak efficiency, η^*, can be pretty well ruled out because of its essentially dependent nature; besides, even though it involves no length, its dependence on shape is weak. The optimum-point value of gH/N^2D^2 can hardly be preferred to Q/ND^3, for it depends almost as strongly on D and is a considerably weaker function of shape.

The best choice is a combination of Q/ND^3 and gH/N^2D^2 that eliminates D. Such a parameter may be formed as follows:

$$\left(\frac{Q}{ND^3}\right)^{\frac{1}{2}}\left(\frac{gH}{N^2D^2}\right)^{-\frac{3}{4}} = \frac{N\sqrt{Q}}{(gH)^{\frac{3}{4}}}. \qquad (13\text{-}32)$$

This parameter exhibits a strong dependence on shape and, of course, no dependence on choice of a size parameter.

Usually the number represented by Eq. (13-32) is not itself used; a closely associated parameter called specific speed is used instead:

$$N_s = \frac{N\sqrt{Q}}{H^{3/4}}. \tag{13-33}$$

Since specific speed is just the number of Eq. (13-32) with g left out, it has all the force of a dimensionless number, provided that the acceleration of gravity doesn't change. Because N_s is not truly dimensionless, the units of N, Q, and H must be specified; the usual choice of units is revolutions per minute, gallons per minute, and feet, respectively. It is called specific speed because it can be identified as the speed at which a model would operate if it were scaled to deliver a flow rate of unity under a head of unity. It is common, though not invariable, to consider it to have the same units as N (as its name and associated interpretation would suggest). If so, Eq. (13-33) would have to be regarded as a numerical equation, incomplete from the standpoint of units.

With specific speed defined, a lot may be said about the family of pumps under consideration without any mention of size or shape of the pump. The relation between peak efficiency and specific speed is dependent only on how the pump performs and not on how it is described physically; so also are the relations between the shapes of the performance curves and specific speed. Using the equations of the last section, we may write equations of the form

$$\eta^* = f(N_s^*), \tag{13-34}$$

$$\frac{H}{H^*} = f\left(\frac{Q}{Q^*}, N_s^*\right). \tag{13-35}$$

The nature of these relations is not influenced by an arbitrary choice of a size or shape parameter. A big advantage of such representations is that they may reveal similarity of performance that might go undiscovered otherwise. It has been found, for example, that the whole range of commercial hydrodynamic pumps from narrow-passage radial-flow pumps to wide-passage axial-flow pumps fit surprisingly well into correlations of the sort described (although the influence of Reynolds number may not be completely ignored). It might possibly have been anticipated that the changes in configuration of such a range of pumps could be described by a single shape parameter, but it would certainly not have been obvious how to select it.

Although one may in this manner avoid including size and shape parameters in certain performance correlations, the question of their proper choice is not thereby rendered unimportant. It would still be valuable to know how specific speed depends on shape and how head or flow rate is related to size and shape. The effective value of D would need to be selected so that gH^*/N^2D^2 or Q^*/ND^3 came out as a function of specific speed alone; then b could be selected to render b/D another function of specific speed alone. If such selections were possible, head, flow, and specific speed could be evaluated in terms of two functions of shape; for example,

$$N_s^* = f_1\left(\frac{b}{D}\right), \tag{13-36}$$

$$H^* = N^2D^2f_2\left(\frac{b}{D}\right), \tag{13-37}$$

$$Q^* = ND^3f_1^2f_2^{3/2}. \tag{13-38}$$

The beauty of characterizing size or shape by consideration of performance—either by direct use of a performance parameter or through equivalence to a standard system—is that it delimits the troublesome problem of physical description. Rather than pervading the whole of the picture, the direct influence of description is minimized and may be expressed as a discrete problem. As a result, a different choice of geometric description leaves much of the picture intact; furthermore, the choice is made easier. Often, of course, the whole idea may prove worthless; but it's still a good idea.

Index

235